NIELS STENSEN

NIELS STENSEN
1638–1686
The Scientist who was beatified

Hans Kermit

GRACEWING

This work was first published in Norwegian under the title
Niels Stensen – Naturforsker og helgen by the
University of Tromso, 1998

First published in English 2003

Gracewing
2 Southern Avenue, Leominster
Herefordshire HR6 0QF

Illustrations on pp. 6, 9, 11, 13, 17, 20, 22, 27, 32, 36, 45, 48, 58, 65, 85 and 96 are reproduced by kind permission of The Royal Library of Copenhagen; on pp. 94 and 99 by kind permission of Troels Kardel and on p. 101 by kind permission of the late Harald Moe.

Cover illustration:
Portrait of Niels Stensen by Christian August Lorentzen (1749–1828).
By kind permission of the University of Copenhagen.

ISBN 0 85244 583 0

Typeset by Action Publishing Technology Ltd,
Gloucester GL1 5SR

Printed by Antony Rowe Ltd,
Eastbourne BN23 6QT

Contents

Note on Text

In addition to his scientific and theological publications around 500 of Stensen's letters have been preserved. This represents the bulk of his copious correspondence in five different languages. The letters were translated into Danish and published by Harriet M. Hansen in 1987, in a book entitled *Niels Stensen's korrespondence i dansk oversettelse* ('Niels Stensen's correspondence: a Danish translation'). Here the letters are numbered chronologically: E1, E2 etc. A manuscript from Stensen's time at University in Copenhagen, the 'Chaos' manuscript, is preserved and in 1997 was translated into English and published by August Ziggelar: *Niels Stensen's Chaos manuscript, Copenhagen, 1959. Complete edition*. The individual notes are numbered N1, N2 etc.

Preface

It is now over ten years since Niels Stensen, the Danish natural scientist and priest, was beatified by Pope John Paul II. Stensen lived in the seventeenth century and won an international reputation in anatomy and as a founder of both geology and palaeontology. He is deemed to be one of the greatest scientists of his age. At the height of his scientific career, Stensen chose to become a Catholic priest and later allowed himself to be consecrated a bishop. His choice was not a rejection of science. Rather he felt called to a greater task, that of working amongst the weakest in society. His ideal became that of evangelical poverty.

His life was full of vicissitudes. His triumphs as researcher and scientist were brief. For long periods he suffered misfortune and loneliness. He lived, for most of his adult life, outside Denmark: principally in Italy, the Netherlands, France and Germany. He travelled several times across the European continent and during his journeys became acquainted with contemporary leaders in science, philosophy and theology.

Stensen's holistic view of science – that it cannot be confined to a single discipline, but must be set within a broader context – resonates today. He sought, without compromise, to expose the truth, his research being based on the thesis of Descartes, that one must question everything. Yet, for Stensen, there was no conflict between science and belief. For him they were but two sides of the same object. Shortly before he became a priest, he stated in a lecture, what many have seen as encapsulating the essence of his life: 'That which we see is beautiful, that which we understand is even more beautiful, but the most beautiful of all is that which we cannot grasp.'.

In the literature, Niels Stensen's name appears in many guises: Niels Steensen, Nicolo Sténon, Niccolò Stenone, Nicholas Steno and often just Steno. He himself used the correct Latin form of Nicolaus Stenonis. As a result, his place in encyclopedias and historical works must be sought under different heads. Kaspar Kallan has written an article on the reason for these many variants of Stensen's name. It can be found in the bibliography of this book.

At the University Library in Tromsø, a tradition has developed of publishing a book in connection with its major annual exhibition. I have taken this opportunity to write a biography of this fascinating character. To produce such a work has involved the collection of information from a large number of academics and private individuals in Tromsø, Trondheim, Copenhagen and Århus. I owe them a deep debt of gratitude for their interest and understanding throughout the period I have been engaged on this project.

Hans Kermit
Tromsø
November 1998

Preface to the English Edition

It now is fifteen years since Pope John Paul II beatified Niels Stensen in Rome and this book is published to honour that occasion. The many written notes which are found on Stensen's sarcophagus in Florence, bear witness that his life and example is an inspiration to many.

It is 330 years since Niels Stensen held his famous Prooemium or Preface to a Demonstration in the Copenhagen Anatomical Theatre in 1673. The speech is a praise to the beauty of the Creator's work and emphasizes that for Stensen there was no conflict between faith and knowledge. He is the only scientist who was beatified.

Stensen travelled many times across the European continent and made friends with several British scientists and scholars, but he himself never visited the British Isles. Thanks to the Royal Society in London, Stensen's major scientific works were reviewed and translated into English, thus making many of his discoveries well known as the news spread rapidly.

I have added most of the new information on Niels Stensen and his contemporaries which has been made available since the original edition of this book was published five years ago.

Hans Kermit
Tromsø
February 2003

The Beatification

Rome, 23 October 1988

An autumn Sunday morning in Rome. The sun is high in the sky. It shines for most of the day, being hidden only now and again by a build-up of black clouds. Brief thunderstorms send rain and hail beating down on the town's paving stones, which become soaking wet. People in the streets take shelter under umbrellas and in Rome's many colonnades and wait until the downpour has passed. The wait is brief. Within half an hour the streets are dry again, the air warm. The locals dress according to the season, but for those of us from Scandinavia it is like a summer's day. Many have already spent a week here and enjoyed much of what the city has to offer. Others flew in on Saturday. Most people are moving in the same direction, towards St Peter's church, where we too are going. People from all directions, dressed for the occasion, enter the church. They are both joyous and solemn at the same time.

For a short while, before the eyes have become accustomed to the gloom, one sees little in the semi-darkness of the church. Still it is difficult to miss the huge aspersorium in the shape of a seashell, or the many marble statues. The central aisle is blocked off and uniformed security guards face the public. One is surprised that they are carrying weapons even in a church. On each chair reserved for our little delegation from Norway and Sweden there lies a small book with a beautiful handwritten medieval text on the front. In addition to the service texts we find a short biography, printed in Italian, German and Danish, of the man whose memory we shall celebrate today – Niels Stensen.

From our seat we see Michelangelo's fantastic dome and the High Altar with its four black columns which stretch an unbelievable thirty-five metres in the air. And yet their size is just right; the proportions are so finely determined that one can easily forget just how huge everything is.

Gradually the church becomes all but full, the congregation of 10,000 are seated. The priests and bishops who are to conduct the service troop along the central aisle in threes. All are dressed in green, which is the colour worn for public worship at this time of year. Suddenly the floodlights along the ceiling are turned on and it becomes as light inside the church as outside. Pope John Paul II enters, followed by those in charge of the service, the same men who will attend him on his visit to Scandinavia the following year. A troop of the Swiss Guard bring up the rear of the procession. They have laid aside their swords, the sheaths on their belts are empty. So as soon as the Pope's white-clad form is visible, the organ and choir burst into the opening hymn. The Pope blesses the congregation with the sign of the cross and the Mass begins with the opening prayer and the confession of sins. After which he takes his place at the High Altar. The choice for the occasion is the Latin Gregorian service, sung antiphonally.

After the readings from the Scriptures, all rise and Bishop Averkamp from Osnabrück and Bishop Hans Ludwig Martensen from Copenhagen move forward to the High Altar. Avekamp gives a short account of Niels Stensen's life in German, concluding in Latin with a plea to the Pope to beatify him.[1] After that Martensen makes the same appeal in Danish. The Pope sits down and

---

[1] The text reads in Latin: *Beatissime Pater, Ordinarius Osnabrügensis humilimle a Sanctitate tua petit at Venerabilem Servum Dei Nicolaum Stensen, numero adscribere Beatorum benigissime digneris.* I, Bishop of Osnabrück, request that Niels Stensen, God's humble servant, be entered amongst the blessed.

declares officially that Niels Stensen shall be counted amongst the blessed and that he will be celebrated annually on the day of his death, 25 November. Two pictures of Niels Stensen, which have been kept under wraps, are now unveiled – one inside the church and the other outside the main door. The exclamation of joy from the many assembled in St Peter's Square is heard as a distant echo inside the church.

For the first time in over 400 years a Scandinavian has been beatified. In total only twenty men and women from the Nordic countries have been accorded such an honour in the whole of Christianity's 2000 years. It is, in truth, an historic moment.

Later that evening as we went to the postbox to send greetings to those at home, a man who had also been in St Peter's, came over to us. He was able to tell us that the beatification had been the first item on the day's news bulletin, and that it had lasted for a couple of minutes.

Niels Stensen, who had been dead for more than 300 years had, for an instant, taken the top spot on the day's news. Why should he today be reckoned amongst the blessed? What was it in this man's life that brought him this singular status? Who on earth was this man?

The life of Niels Stensen

The goldsmith's son

Niels Stensen was born on New Year's Day 1638 in Klareboderne, a little street in Copenhagen, not far from the Round Tower. The building of the latter had barely begun. It was completed in 1642. The tower was the first public observatory in Europe, an element in a far-reaching expansion of the University which King Christian IV had set in train. Niels Stensen's father, Sten Pedersen, was a goldsmith. The male members of his family – it came from what is now the Swedish province of Skåne – had traditionally chosen the cloth. Sten had not done so, choosing instead to move to Copenhagen, where he operated a goldsmith's workshop and sold a little wine on the side. He was an able goldsmith who supplied many items to the court of Christian IV, several of his beautiful works being still preserved.[2] Niels' mother, Anne Nielsdatter, came from the Danish province of Fyn. She was a childless widow when she married Sten Pedersen. Together they produced Niels, and a daughter Anne. Sten Pedersen had two children from an earlier marriage, Lisbeth and Johan.

By the standards of the time, Copenhagen was then a large town with between 20,000 and 30,000 inhabitants. The total rose and fell sharply as epidemics, which could

[2] Chalices bearing Sten Pedersen's signature are to be found in Holmen's Church, Copenhagen, in Valle Church, Aust-Agder and in Vinslöv Church, Skåne. A wine decanter made by Sten Pedersen has also been found in the Russian Tsar's treasury.

reduce it by several thousand, took their toll. Even under normal conditions, mortality was high, but thanks to heavy migration from the countryside, the population was sustained. Urban hygiene was poor. The sight of rats and mice roaming freely in the streets must have been a daily occurrence, whilst sanitation, viewed from today's perspective, was but a joke.

Niels Stensen was an unassuming boy who suffered from poor health. Later he was to write that he had had a chronic illness as a child that prevented him from playing out with his peers. He was, therefore, protected by his parents and older friends and soon became accustomed to hearing serious, adult conversation. His contemporaries described him as 'small and sickly', with a frail disposition. His health must, however, have improved considerably with age, for as an adult he was able to withstand numerous shocks and strains.

The family's property in Copenhagen was described as a sizeable residence, though it was small relative to most of the neighbouring properties, which belonged to the aristocracy. Sten Pedersen, however, was prosperous belonging, as he did, to the upper middle class. He would, perhaps, have been rich had Christian IV paid him all he owed. The workshop supplied much gold and silver ware to the royal household, but the Danish King spent far too much on building works and participation in the Thirty Years War, so the kingdom was constantly short of money. Even if the King debased the currency by mixing silver with less precious metals, he was still not able to meet all his obligations. The result was that his suppliers had to wait patiently for payment for their goods and services. Sten Pedersen was much appreciated by the King, both for his artistic talent and, as his son was to relate later, because he was a cultured and God-fearing man.

Klareboderne, which was a side street of Købmagergade, the main street in Copenhagen at that time, still bears the name. In 1997 a memorial plaque was placed on the site of the goldsmith's workshop to indicate that here

The goldsmith's workshop in the seventeenth century. It was in the workshop that Niels became acquainted with the world of metal and learned the significance of precision and practice if a craftsman was to produce a good piece of work.

was the place where Niels Stensen was born. Opposite the workshop and vintner's stood a large townhouse , where Peder Schumacher was born a couple of years before Niels Stensen. He was the son of a German wine merchant and a highly gifted child. At the age of twelve he took the University entrance exam and studied theology, medicine and political science. He became librarian to Frederick III and was later made the Kingdom's Chancellor. Schumacher was one of the century's greatest statesmen. He was raised to the peerage under the name of Griffenfeld and granted the earldom of Tønsberg. During the war with Sweden in 1676 he was accused of high treason and condemned to death. This was commuted to life imprisonment at the place of execution, a sentence that was served on Munkholmen in Trondheim's fjord. No-one knows if Niels and Peder had been childhood friends, but that they knew each other is certain.

Niels was seven years old when his father died. His mother re-married, first to the goldsmith Peder Lesle who did not live very long and then to the goldsmith Johan Stichmann. He was a skilled craftsman who soon built up his business. After his father's death, Jørgen Carstensen, who was clerk of the Exchequer, was made Niels' guardian. He had been married to Niels' elder half-sister, Lisbeth, who had died in 1644. He took good care of his ward and ensured that he got his share of an inheritance from some relatives in Skåne. There is conflicting evidence as to whether Niels continued to live with his mother and stepfather or moved in with Carstensen. In any case it is certain that Niels was often to be found in the goldsmith's workshop in Klareboderne. He enjoyed good relations with his stepfather who paid for his education.

As a ten-year-old, Niels was sent to the School of Our Lady, one of the country's leading classical establishments. Here too came the children of government servants and the wealthy of Norway and Iceland. The name later changed to the Metropolitan School. It still continues as a grammar school in Copenhagen. Teaching took place in a single large room, with no walls separating the different classes. In the seventeenth century the school was largely financed from money received for the choral work the boys carried out at church services. When Niels began school it had around 500 pupils. The headmaster, Jørgen Eilersen, was a gifted teacher and his pupils received an excellent education in both the classical languages and mathematics. Ole Borch was one of Niels' teachers, or ushers as they were then called. Borch had studied medicine but, at the same time, he pursued his interests in botany, chemistry and classical languages. He was a gifted linguist and published a textbook on how to write poetry in Latin. He often took his pupils on botanical expeditions – they appeared as 'nature walks' on the timetable – in the districts around Copenhagen. Borch was also interested in chemistry and in 1655 he left the school to take up a position with the High Steward as private tutor and administrator of a chemistry laboratory, which he also used for his own research. Niels often visited his old teacher in his new home and followed his experiments. From surviving notes made by Stensen during his years of study, we know that he also conducted chemical experiments in the goldsmith's workshop, where he had a great deal of apparatus and chemicals at his disposal. Such instructive visits provide some of the context for Niels' early interest in the natural sciences. Their common interest in science brought them together in a close friendship which lasted for life. Both Borch and Eilersen were later to become professors at the University.

These were troubled times for Denmark as a result of its involvement in the Thirty Years War and frequent conflicts with Sweden. Several dangerous diseases, such as dysentery and bubonic plague, raged periodically in Copenhagen at this time, sharply raising levels of mortality. Ole Worm, professor of medicine, noted that the bubonic plague had broken out again in April 1654. Approximately half the schoolchildren and one third of the town's general population died from the disease. The

Ole Borch with his pupils on a botanical expedition on the outskirts of Copenhagen. '. . . We went out with Dr. Borch to look for herbs we could recognise and walked almost 10 kilometres', writes one of Stensen's fellow students (Jørgensen 1884). The drawing is taken from Holger Jacobæus' travel book of 1672.

Latin School earned huge sums from its pupils singing at the numerous funerals: every effort was made to provide a dignified Christian burial. The bells tolled from morning till night when the plague was at its height and on some days the pupils took part in up to sixty funerals.

As a boy Niels became friendly with Jakob Henrik Paulli who lived in Studiestræde, not far from the cathedral in Copenhagen. Writing many years later of Jakob Henrik, who was a year older than him, Niels noted: 'He was the son of His Majesty's senior physician and, as a boy, I was brought up with him in Copenhagen.' Jakob Henrik was the eldest son of Simon Paulli, formerly a German professor from Rostock and now personal physician to Frederick III. Paulli's father-in-law, Jacob Fabricius had enjoyed the same position with Christian IV and had prevailed upon the King to give his son-in-law a professorship at the University of Copenhagen. Simon Paulli told the King that he was willing to lecture in anatomy and to carry out the dissection of dead animals and humans. No medical professor was willing to do this in Denmark at that time, since contemporary norms did not permit decent people to mix with those who cut up corpses. Doctors educated at the University of Copenhagen had to travel abroad to witness dissections. At that time surgeons and barber-surgeons had no medical training and their knowledge of anatomy was very slight. Several years earlier, a committee set up by the University had drawn attention to the situation, and recommended improvements in the teaching of anatomy. Christian IV was, therefore, interested in Simon Paulli's offer. As a result he was given a personal chair in botany, anatomy and surgery, paid out of the King's own pocket.

One of the older university buildings was refurbished to become Denmark's first anatomy department, the Domus Anatomica. It was opened for public dissections in 1644. Beside the anatomy theatre was a room devoted specifically to the preparation of the bodies for the demonstrations, as well as a small room where the instruments

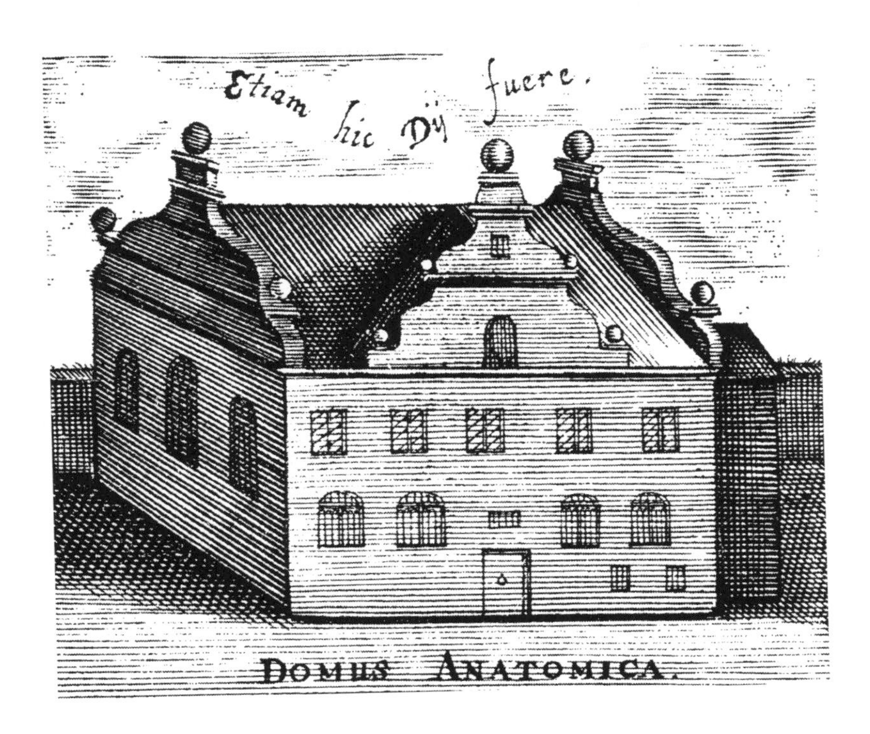

Domus Anatomica ('The Anatomy House') which was used for lectures in anatomy and public dissections at the University of Copenhagen from 1644. Previously students had to go abroad to receive teaching in this subject. The House contained a dissection room, the anatomical theatre, a preparation room, a room for instruments and one for the preservation of bodies.

were stored and where the lecturer could 'arrange his thoughts and his clothes prior to the public demonstration'. In the anatomy theatre itself, Theatrum Anatomicum, there was a dissection table that could be rotated and seats for the spectators arranged in the form of an amphitheatre. A special box was prepared for the King, as Paulli hoped he would be present at the dissections. The back wall was decorated with a symbolic representation of the tree of knowledge with a snake in stone. On each side stood a human skeleton, one a man, the other a woman – Adam and Eve. There were animal skeletons too. The whole design of the anatomy theatre was based on overseas models.

It was not easy for the German Simon Paulli to gain the respect of the medical establishment at the University. Distrust was hardly diminished when he began to dissect bodies and urged not only doctors, but theologians, barber-surgeons and the interested 'of all classes' to attend the demonstrations. Instruction was in German, as the barber-surgeons, and many other members of the audience, did not understand Latin, which was the academic language of the day and Simon Paulli was not very fluent in Danish. Paulli had aimed to make the teaching of anatomy acceptable, and he succeeded. It was a great success. People had to pay to attend the dissections – as if they were theatrical performances – something which incensed the other professors of medicine. But Paulli needed the money, as Jakob Henrik eventually had fourteen brothers and sisters!

When Christian IV died in 1648, Simon Paulli lost his professorship and had to turn to building up a practice as an ordinary doctor. After some years, however, he became King Frederick III's personal physician. He now had the opportunity to pursue his great interest in botany. He collected plants for a large herbarium and published *Flora Danica*, an illustrated catalogue of medicinal plants from Norway and Denmark.

Here Niels was able to share in the scholarly ambience

Admission tokens to the demonstrations in the Anatomy House. The public demonstrations held by Simon Paulli were a great success and it became fashionable to attend them – there being, at the time, something theatrical about them.

of Paulli's home, not least through all the books he found there. Later Niels Stensen was to speak of Simon Paulli with great respect. In a letter to the Dutch doctor, Willen Piso, dated 1664, he writes of Simon Paulli as: 'that highly regarded royal doctor and prelate in Århus, my teacher Simon Paulli, whom I revere as a son would'.[E 15]

Student at the University of Copenhagen

In 1656, Niels Stensen, along with twenty-one other boys from the Latin School, successfully sat the University entrance exam and was matriculated at the University of Copenhagen. At that time most studied theology, a sure way of getting an official position as a priest. Stensen, however, chose to study medicine. His close contact with Ole Broch and Simon Paulli, who were both doctors, undoubtedly influenced his choice.

The University had been founded in 1479 by Christian I and was, for several hundred years, the centre for all academic work in the joint kingdom of Denmark-Norway. After a period of decline, the quality of the teaching in medicine and natural sciences had improved considerably in the seventeenth century. This was due above all to the famous Bartholin family, many of whom were clever and justly renowned academics. For over a hundred years they were to set their stamp on the University of Copenhagen. The most famous member of the family was Thomas Bartholin, an anatomist who achieved an international reputation for his discovery of the lymph duct. As well as holding chairs in medicine and anatomy, he was also professor of mathematics and Dean of the Medical Faculty. It was whilst he was Dean that he did much to enhance the discipline in the University. He founded Scandinavia's first academic journal, *Acta Medica & Philosophica Hafniensia*. He was also the prime mover in the preparation of the first medical law and pharmocopoeia in Denmark-Norway. On beginning study at the University, students usually chose a moral tutor who would take responsibility for monitoring their progress during their study years. The tutor had also to keep an eye on a student's general conduct and could punish those who misbehaved. Stensen chose Thomas Bartholin as his tutor. The two became friends, a friendship which, at least on Niels Stensen's side, never faltered.

Denmark-Norway had to cede almost a third of her territory by the terms of the Peace of Brömsebro in 1645 and of Roskilde in 1658: Skåne, Halland and Blekinge to the east of the Øresund and the fiefdoms of Bohus and Trondhjem as well as Jemtland and Herjedalen in Norway. The winter of 1657–58 had been a very cold one, so cold, in fact, that the sea froze over and Charles Gustav X was able to cross over the ice with his army from Jutland to the islands of Fyn and Sjælland and so threaten Copenhagen. In this way the Swedes had won an easy victory and a very advantageous peace with Denmark-Norway at Roskilde. In spite of this Charles Gustav reproached himself for making peace, and five months later he took his army overland to attack Copenhagen. A huge Swedish fleet cut off Copenhagen from all contact with the outside world by sea. The army of Denmark-Norway was not on a war footing. The population of Copenhagen panicked when, on 8 August, it became known that Charles Gustav had broken the peace. Whilst its citizens helped fortify and defend the town, messages were sent post haste to the Netherlands requesting help.

Thomas Bartholin, who lived in Roskilde, was unable to attend the University of Copenhagen during the time that the town was besieged – almost two years. As a result his brother Rasmus Bartholin had to take on some of his teaching. Rasmus was a great admirer of Descartes and, without doubt his views influenced the young Niels Stensen. As a result of the long siege of Copenhagen by the Swedes, the University was finally forced to close and the students to take part in the defence of the town.

Student brigades were formed and Stensen was

enrolled in the Norwegian Brigade, so called because of the large number of Norwegian students who were members of it.

After the war ended the King, in 1661, granted privileges to many of Copenhagen's leading citizens as thanks for their contribution to the defence of the capital.

For the period of the war, Stensen had to study on his own, alongside his duties in the defence of Copenhagen. The students were mainly employed as sentries at night, on the walls around the town. The winter of 1658–59 was unusually cold and the students had only small braziers to warm themselves. The siege resulted in shortages of everything – including fuel – so light and warmth from the braziers was the exception rather than the rule. It was not easy to study under such circumstances. To help him to remember things, Nielsen began to make notes. They cover the period from 8 March 1659 to 3 July of the same year and amount to ninety-two folio pages. They were found by chance in 1946 in Florence, together with Galileo Galilei's posthumous works. They have since been given the title of the 'Chaos' manuscript, because under the words 'In the name of Jesus' (*In nomine Jesu*) at the top of the first page we find the title 'Chaos', presumably referring to the wide variety of subject matter in the notes.

The manuscript is an important source for our understanding of Stensen's years at university, consisting, as it does, of extracts from academic works, notes of experiments, reports of conversations and short religious observations. The notes indicate that the student Stensen had read nearly 100 books, in whole or in part, by some eighty authors, including Kepler, Galileo, Borelli, Descartes and many who are unknown today. In addition to the books in the University libraries, Stensen had access to the private collections of, for example, Simon Paulli and Ole Broch. The notes also contain short comments of a more personal nature such as 'nothing done today'. Only very recently has the entire 'Chaos' manuscript been subject to analysis.

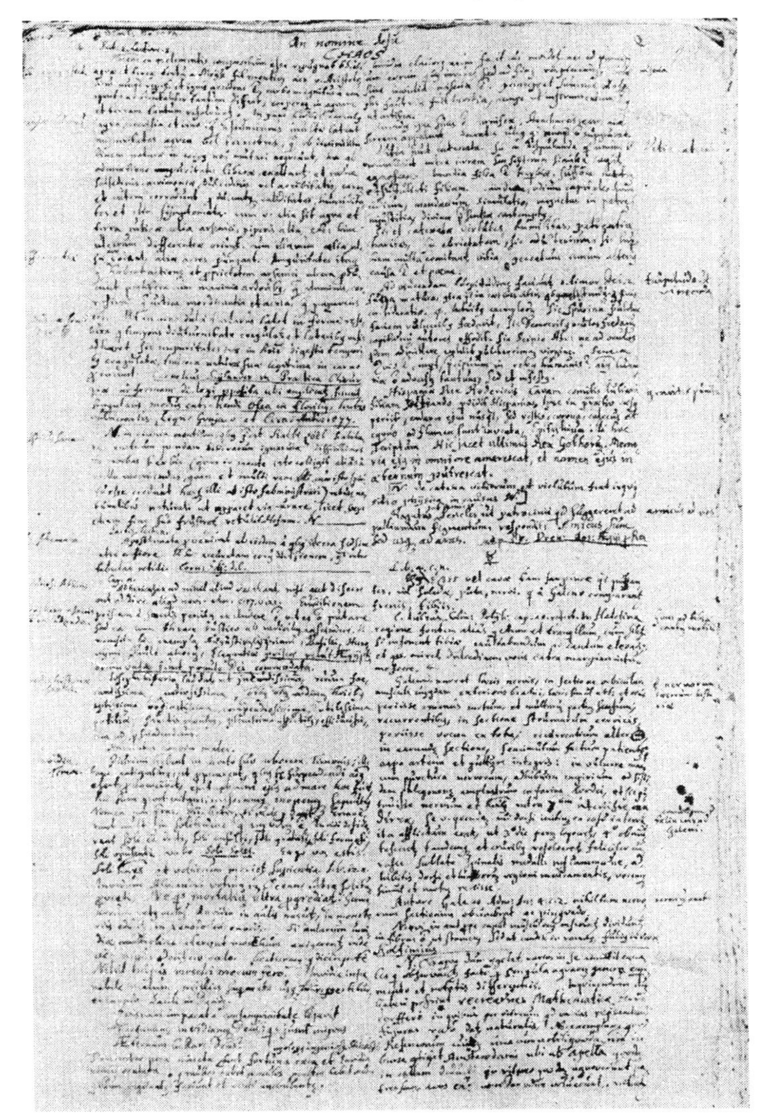
In nomine Jesu

Chaos

First page of the 'Chaos' manuscript which Stensen wrote during the war year of 1659. The notes, which are written in Latin, were first discovered in 1946, and are one of the few sets of notes written by a Danish student in the seventeenth century that are still in existence. Stensen refers to almost all contemporary works in natural science and philosophy.

Anatomical studies in the Netherlands

In the autumn of 1659 the war moved towards its close and the siege of Copenhagen was partially lifted. It was again possible to leave the town. Records indicate that the first passports were issued on 18 September to thirty-one students who, because of a shortage of money, wanted to return to their homes in Jutland or in Norway. The twenty-two year-old Niels Stensen also took the opportunity to leave town and with letters of recommendation from Thomas Bartholin and Simon Paulli, he travelled on or around 1 December to Germany and the Netherlands, in order to continue his education. As teaching in anatomy was no longer available at the University of Copenhagen, would-be doctors had to take their final examinations at a foreign university. Stensen first travelled by sea to Rostock where, for a few months, he attended lectures in medicine. Then he took the long journey by stagecoach to Hamburg, continuing via Bremen, to Amsterdam, where he arrived just as peace was concluded between Sweden and Denmark-Norway.

It was not by accident that he travelled to the Netherlands. The country was a great power both politically and culturally. It was also one of the richest countries in Europe and was regarded as a leading nation in science and art. In the realm of painting, Dutch artists were reckoned to be amongst the finest. Rembrandt, the country's greatest painter, was still active when Stensen first became acquainted with the Europe of scholarship. The Netherlands had also been an ally of Denmark in the war with Sweden and had won a permanent place in the hearts of Danes, because it was the Dutch fleet that helped lift the siege of Copenhagen.

Amsterdam was four to five times the size of Copenhagen, a centre for trade and shipping. The young student found here, for the first time, a proper hospital. There was no such thing at that time in Scandanavia. There were, however, a number of ad hoc arrangements. Leprosy had come to Europe with the returning Crusaders in the thirteenth century and Houses of St George had been set up to take care of lepers. During major epidemics, ordinary houses were turned into temporary 'plague houses', in which the sick could be isolated. And in wartime both the army and navy commandeered houses, to take care of the injured. The first proper hospital in Norway was established in Kristiania in 1743; Frederick's Hospital was established in Copenhagen in 1759.

Anatomy was taught at Amsterdam's Atheneum. Dissections were carried out during the winter half-year in an attic of one of the town's meat markets, where a room was furnished with benches and instruments for cutting up corpses. Thanks to his letter of recommendation from Bartholin, Stensen was able to lodge with Gerhard Blasius, the professor of anatomy. He was a close friend of Bartholin, had studied medicine in Copenhagen and spoke Danish.

During his stay, Stensen made his first scientific discovery. After an everyday teaching session had ended, he dissected a sheep's head and discovered the duct conveying the parotid gland, *ductus parotideus*. The parotid gland, *parotis*, lies in the cheek of humans and most mammals, and provides the oral cavity with most of the saliva needed to break down food. By guiding a probe through the duct he found that it opened into the mouth opposite the second to last molar of the upper jaw. Stensen told Blasius of his discovery, but after the latter had looked up the literature and found that this duct had not previously been written up, he dismissed the whole as a shoddy piece of work. Several days later, Stensen repeated the exercise, this time with a dog's head and came to the same result – the excretary duct of the parotid gland opened into the mouth opposite the second to last molar of the upper jaw. At first only friends learned of the discovery, including Bartholin to whom Stensen wrote. He never mentioned it again to Blasius.

Even though his stay in Amsterdam lasted no more than

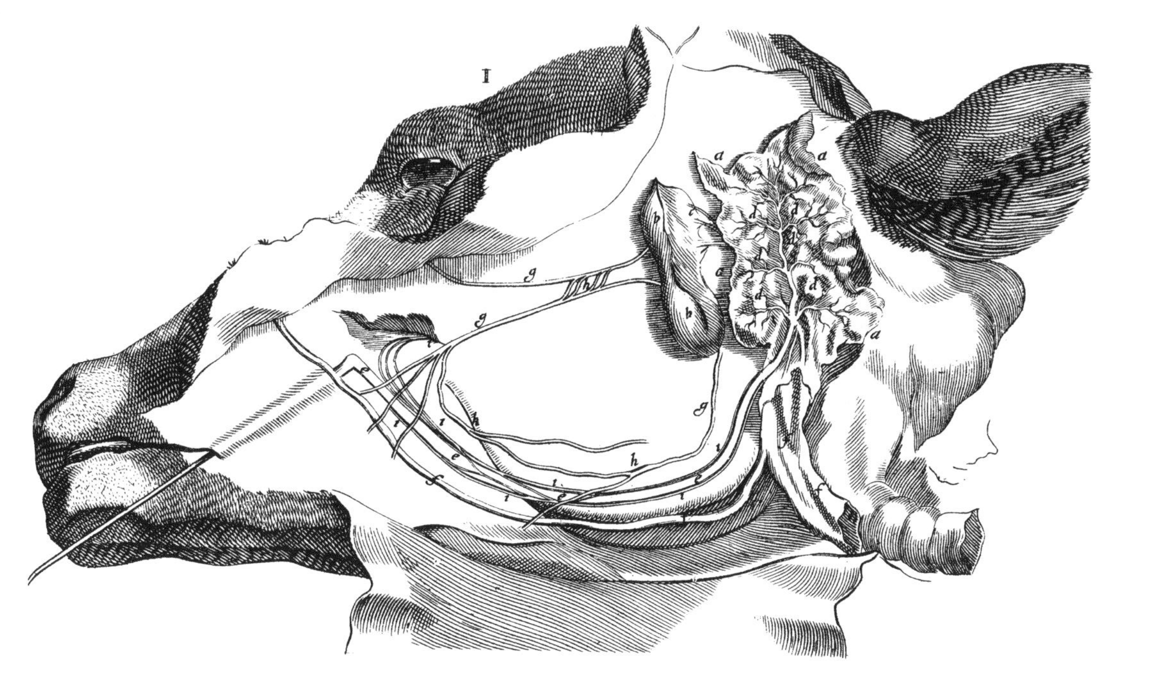

Stensen's drawing of the perotid duct of a calf. The probe that projects from the mouth, is inserted in the duct, marked (e) on the figure. Branches of the duct (d) are shown in the opened gland. Stensen called the first discovery *inventiunicula* – a little observation. Professor van Horne in Leiden gave it the name *Stensen's duct*.

four months, Stensen enjoyed a number of close contacts both with fellow students and some notable figures, a testimony to his personality and charm. In 1660 he moved on to Leiden where he was admitted to the University. At that time Leiden was much bigger than it is today. Chronicles of the town tell us that there were then 13,000 houses, 200 streets, 25 canals and 120 bridges. The University was the oldest in the Netherlands, having been founded in 1575 by William the Silent, and had won a reputation as a teaching centre for medicine and natural science. The distinguished Professor François de la Boë Sylvius, head of the teaching of clinical medicine, was an able teacher, known for his contribution to the study of the lymph gland and the brain. At this time he had, in addition to Niels Stensen, several outstanding students including insectologist Jan Swammerdam, physiologist de Graaf and the medical doctor Theodor Kerckring. At the start of anatomy teaching, Stensen told Sylvius of his discovery of the duct of the parotid gland. Sylvius, together with another famous professor of anatomy, Jan van Horne, was quickly able to establish the existence of the organ, both in humans and other animals. Van Horne called the excretary duct the *ductus stenonianus*, a name by which it is still known today. After Stensen left Amsterdam, Blasius published a book in which he described the parotid duct as his own discovery. The publication brought about a war of words between Stensen and Blasius as to whom had first made the discovery. From surviving correspondence between Stensen and Bartholin we know that Stensen took this badly. Later he was to write of this period:

> At the beginning I felt bitter and hard done by, but as I was blameless, I put up with these trials. I did my best to defend myself. Although on several occasions I had a good opportunity to fight back, and was often encouraged to do so, God freed me from thoughts of revenge. (*Op. Theol.* I, p. 392).

Print of the University of Leiden which in the middle of the seventeenth century was the leading university in northern Europe. The tall University building was furnished with the very latest equipment and had a library, botanical garden and anatomy theatre. In the streets the students can be seen with their characteristic capes and broad rimmed hats.

NICOLAI STENONIS
OBSERVATIONES
ANATOMICÆ,
QUIBUS
Varia Oris, Oculorum, & Narium
Vaſa deſcribuntur, novique ſalivæ, lacry-
marum & muci fontes deteguntur,
ET
Novum Nobiliſſimi
B I L S I I
De lymphæ motu & uſu
commentum
Examinatur & rejicitur.

LUGDUNI BATAVORUM,
Apud JACOBUM CHOUËT.
CIↄ Iↄ C LXII.

First page of Stensen's small book on his observations of the glands of the mouth, eye and nose that was published in 1662. It is dedicated to his teachers in Copenhagen and Leiden, amongst which was the mathematics professor Jakob Golius. The book is of modest dimensions, the picture indicating its true size.

Stensen was a young student, whilst Blasius was not only a famous professor of anatomy, but also a good friend of Bartholin. Stensen had lived in Blasius' home and been well received by him. He was now in a difficult situation. On advice from his tutor, he began work on a short essay, in which he would point out the difference between the duct he had discovered and that described by Blasius. But Blasius was not prepared to give up so easily and the quarrel continued over several years. The result was that the duct is still called the *ductus stenonianus*. Subsequently Stensen made much greater discoveries in his time in Leiden, where he published eleven academic essays, being his most fruitful in the sphere of anatomy. Later in life he was to regret his youthful anger.

Stensen continued his anatomical study of the glands in the head and published his results in a thesis: *Anatomical observations of the mouth's glands and newly discovered ducts.* Under Van Horne's guidance, Stensen defended his thesis from 6–9 July 1661, at the University of Leiden. This was his first official publication as an independent researcher.

Ole Borch also came to Leiden, where he had been given a professorship and a scholarship to undertake a study tour overseas. Stensen now took a well-earned summer holiday together with his old teacher. They visited the shipyards at Zaandam and saw how oil was extracted from seed. They also went to Amsterdam where they met Peter Schumacher. During the war with Sweden he had studied political science in England and had come to Amsterdam to complete his studies.

After his holidays, Stensen began to carry out new studies of the glands and on 6 December 1661 the manuscript of his *Observationes anatomicae* was finished. It was published at the beginning of 1662 and contains four essays. Stensen describes his discovery of a series of glands in the eye, ear, nose and mouth, besides the sweat glands. The discoveries occurred so rapidly, one after the other, that publication of the book had to be put off several times. The delay was also due to the fact that the author had to pay the printing costs himself and Stensen had little money. When, finally, it was finished, the book proved to be an outstanding scholarly work in which the bulk of the human body's exocrine[3] glands are described and their function explained. With this work Stensen had, in effect, laid the foundation of the study of glands.

Stensen sent the first copy of the book to Thomas Bartholin. At about the same time Borch wrote to Bartholin, praising Stensen's contribution and drawing attention to his unflagging zeal, his sound judgement and his all-round scholastic skills. He wrote too of his hope that, within a few years, he would be given the task of leading the study of anatomy at the University of Copenhagen. Bartholin replied that he had shown the book to the King and explained its content to him. The King has been gracious enough to listen to Bartholin's expectation that Stensen's fame would come to be tied to the University of Copenhagen.

It was not, however, Stensen who was given a post at the University. In May 1662, Jakob Henrik Paulli – son of Simon Paulli and Stensen's childhood friend – was given the title of professor of anatomy-in-waiting. This meant that he would first take the chair when his studies qualified him to do so. In Scandinavia today this would be called a personal research professorship, normally lasting three years, during which its possessor has to prove his chair-worthiness. Simon Paulli had many children, all of whom had to be found an income. He had used his influence with the King on behalf of his son. Jakob Henrik's output consisted of no more than a couple of poems in praise of the King, whilst Stensen had several academic publications to his name.

---

[3] The exocrine glands empty their secretions through a duct onto one of the body's surfaces. It can be the outer surfaces; the skin, where, for example, the sweat glands excrete sweat, or it can be an inner surface such as the oral cavity or stomach, where the salivary glands and the digestive glands empty.

Meetings with several contemporary philosophers

Religious freedom in the Netherlands had brought about the growth of a welter of religious and philosophical movements. Here the persecuted Spanish Jew found sanctuary alongside French philosophers and broadminded scholars, of whom one was René Descartes. For Stensen, who had been brought up in the Lutheran faith, this religious toleration was wholly new. Lutheranism tolerated no deviation from its understanding of Holy Writ and a dialogue with members of other religious persuasions was unusual at that time in Copenhagen. The intellectual freedom that existed in the Netherlands and which allowed many different views of life to be expressed, could be disturbing for foreigners, but it had the advantage that the discussion of such views meant that one was forced to reflect over one's own. The young Stensen felt a sense of deliverance, but many years later he took the opposite view, when he discovered that the different religious beliefs and sects had led many into a deep religious and moral crisis.

At this period Stensen must have thought about his own situation and career prospects. The appointment of Jakob Henrik Paulli had come as a shock. After having completed several academic works containing important finds in the field of anatomy, he had been passed over for a professorship in anatomy in favour of one who had written nothing. Stensen must have wondered whether or not anatomy was the right discipline for him. The thought of studying mathematics took shape. Perhaps the chance of a permanent position would be enhanced if he deepened his study of mathematics. Besides, geometry was at that time held in higher regard than natural science.

During the years he studied in Leiden, Niels Stensen became acquainted with the famous Jewish philosopher Baruch Spinoza who lived in Rijnsburg, not far from Leiden. Stensen has written, in a document recently found in the Vatican, that the two men became acquainted when

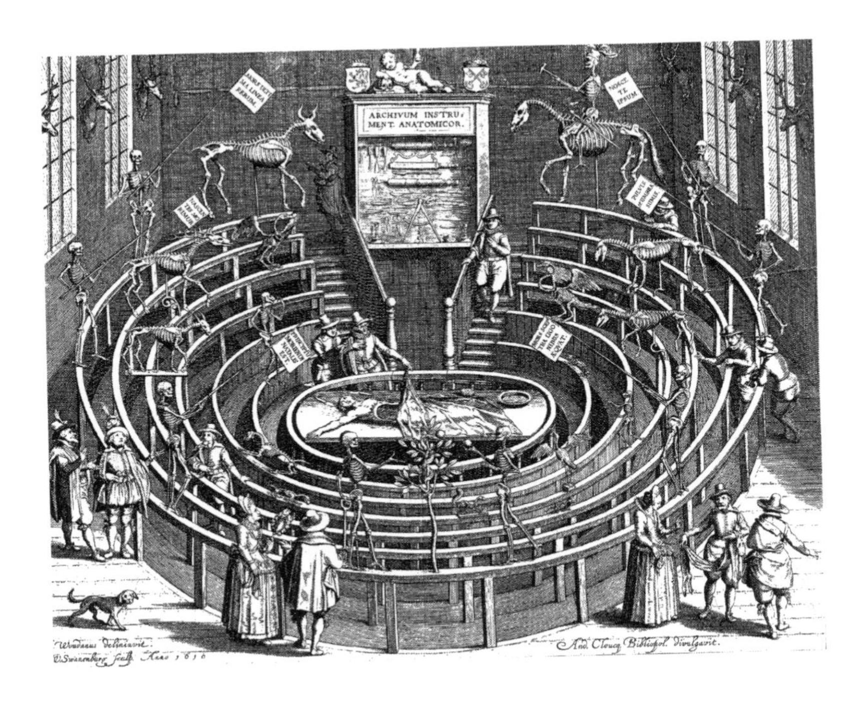

The anatomy theatre in Leiden as it appeared around 1610. The six rows of benches are arranged as an amphitheatre. The two inner rows were reserved for professors and students, the rest being for those of the general public who were interested. When lectures were not being delivered, the room was used for an exhibition of human skeletons, to which were attached placards carrying such small phrases as: 'Birth is the beginning of death', 'The destiny of all things on earth is death', and 'We are but dust and shadows'.

Spinoza was present when the Dane dissected brains (Totaro, 2002). Spinoza came from a Jewish family that had earlier been expelled from Portugal. His father was a respected businessman in Amsterdam. Spinoza showed early signs of brilliance and began to study to be a rabbi but his studies took another direction – towards philosophy. The young Jew's study of Descartes and the natural sciences was seen as playing with fire and led to a break with the synagogue. He moved, therefore, to Rijnsburg, where he lived a spartan existence, several times turning down legacies – and also an offer from the University of Heidelberg – all in an effort to protect his philosophical independence. He worked to improve on Descartes philosophy and earned a living grinding glass for lenses. Stensen was impressed by Spinoza's simple lifestyle and the serenity achieved through following exclusively reason's lead.

Spinoza wanted to formulate a philosophical system based on mathematical principles, wholly geometrical in form. Stensen, who at this time was himself deep into mathematics, was influenced by the philosopher's views and had long conversations with him on both mathematics and philosophy. On matters of belief, however, the two had different opinions. Spinoza was a pantheist, believing that God and nature was the same. Everything could be understood from nature which was itself a unified whole. This conflicted with Stensen's belief in a personal God who had created nature. Spinoza's viewpoint was later to be of great importance for Goethe and the Romantic Movement.

Towards the end of 1662 a posthumous work of Descartes was published – *On Mankind (De homini).* Stensen must have known of its content before publication, for he discusses it in a letter to Thomas Bartholin in May of the same year. In his letter, Stensen praises Descartes' genius, even his mistakes e.g. the theory that tears came from the brain. Summing up, Stensen says that Descartes' account of the human brain stems from a

The University Library in Leiden – founded in 1575 – was one of the best in Europe during the sixteenth century. Books were arranged according to their subject matter and were chained to the bookshelves, which also functioned as reading places. The tall windows ensured plenty of daylight and were placed so that the light fell along the rows of books.

brilliant idea, although it is doubtful if the brain actually functioned in the way he described.

Bartholin, who kept himself informed of Stensen's studies and academic output, encouraged his pupil in a letter to him of August 1662: '... continue with your study of anatomy, as you appear to be born to it, so that it will come to benefit sick people.' Perhaps Bartholin understood that Stensen felt he had come to a crossroads in his life. The appointment of Jakob Henrik Paulli as professor of anatomy caused his cleverest pupil to consider whether or not to give up anatomy, and, instead, take on the study of mathematics at another university.

Other letters came from home. At last, with the ending of the war with Sweden, the goldsmith's workshop in Klareboderne was enjoying better times and Johan Stichmann was able to send more money to prolong Stensen's studies. Stensen decided, therefore, to stay in Leiden and continue with anatomy. Blasius had not given up his attempt to claim the honour of discovering the duct of the parotid gland and renewed his attack on his former pupil. In a letter to Bartholin, Stensen wrote:

> Once I had published my small observations I decided I would lay aside the anatomist's knife till times got better, and take up again the geometrician's compasses, which I had never wholly abandoned [...] even if my limited means commanded, more than advised, me to prefer the useful over the enjoyable. Scarcely had I rinsed the blood from my hands and come in contact with the mathematician's blackboard's delightful dust, than I was met with unpleasant threats from famous men who laid at my door opinions I had never held. They seemed to begrudge me the long lost joy and forced me to answer and to return to the bloody craft.[E 9]

Stenson must have felt challenged as an anatomist when he read the attack by Blasius. But the late Descartes' writings on the anatomy of the brain must also have stimulated him to continue his anatomical enquiries. In his last work – *On Mankind* – Descartes had written about the relationship between the body and the soul. In the brain there is a small gland, the so-called pineal body, *glandula pinealis,* which Descartes believed was the link between the body and the soul in humans. Through the pineal body the two acted on each other with the gland shifting its position vis-à-vis the brain. Animals, on the other hand, had no soul according to Descartes and functioned as pure machines. This inspired Stensen to study the anatomy of the brain, and with incredible energy he now began to dissect many brains from both humans and animals in order to test the theories on the pineal body. It turned out that it was not easy, on the dissection table, to show the link that Descartes had described. Clearly the map was not of the territory. In a letter to Thomas Bartholin dated 5 March, 1663, Stensen speaks about his dissection of a horse, where he had observed the pineal body. He continues

> ... the more brains I open up, some of other animals, some of different kinds of birds, the less likely it seems that the clever and plausible hypothesis regarding the animal brain, serves to explain animal behaviour, in the way the noble Descartes conceived it.[(E 11)]

In this letter Stensen also remarks on the painstaking investigations he was engaged upon into the heart's muscle structure. His next letter to Bartholin, dated 30 April 1663, deals almost exclusively with muscles and the special structure of the heart. His conclusion appears to be clear: 'So far as the substance of the heart is concerned, I will, I believe, be able to provide conclusive evidence of the fact that there is nothing in the heart that is not in the muscle.' By comparing the heart and other muscles in the body, he demonstrated that the structure of the tissue was the same. The heart was a muscle! Stensen proposed to publish his findings in a separate treatise.

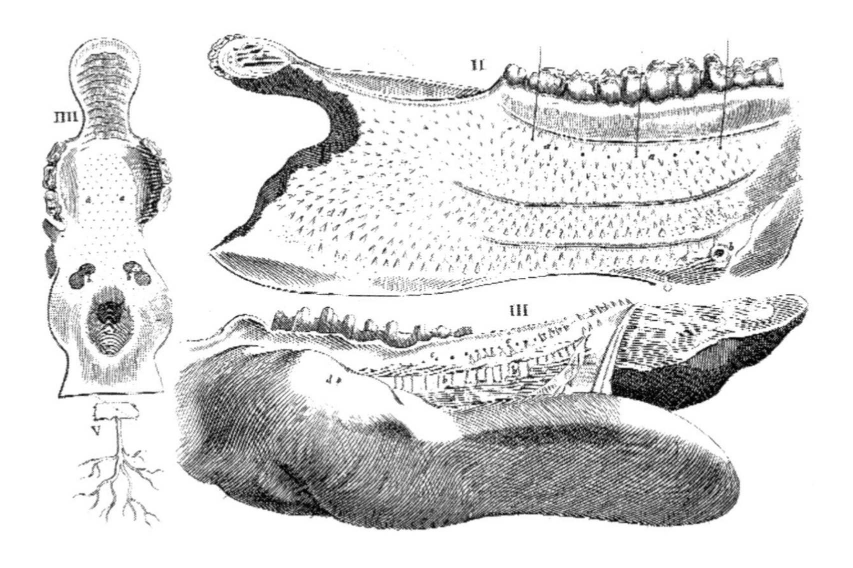

Figures from Stensen's treatise on the glands of the mouth. (II) shows the openings of the ducts (a) from the cheek's salivary gland that comes out under the teeth. In three of them a hair is inserted, and the opening to the parotid duct is marked (b). (III) is a cross section through the mucous membrane between the teeth and the tongue and shows the salivary gland beneath the tongue. About 20 ducts (b) and their exits (c) can be seen above the gland. (IIII) shows the exits of the salivary glands in the head (a). The tonsils are marked (b). (V) shows the course of a duct in one of the cheeks' salivary glands.

Copenhagen and France

The publication of the treatise on muscles and the heart had to be postponed when Stensen learned, towards the end of 1663, that his stepfather, Johan Stichmann, was dead. At short notice he had to interrupt his studies and travel to Copenhagen. He arrived in Denmark in March 1664 and lived with his mother in Klareboderne. In the time that followed, Stensen had several matters to take care of. First he had to complete his work on muscles. Second he had to settle the estate of Johan Stichmann. And then he had to explore the possibility of a position at the University. This last could prove difficult as there were no vacant positions suitable for Stensen.

Stichmann's estate revealed that the King owed him 2500 *riksdaler*, a sizeable sum at that time. Niels Stensen's elder sister, Anne, had married the goldsmith Jakob Kitzerow who owned a house and its associated goldsmith's workshop in Købmagergade. Not long after – in June 1664 – Stensen's mother also died. It was a sad time for him, but there was one bright spot. Jakob Henrik Paulli, who had been appointed professor of anatomy, had decided to give up the discipline and instead teach history. In addition there were a couple of vacant stand-in positions, one in geography, the other in history. Stensen's hope of a university post was not, therefore, entirely unrealistic. He worked hard to finish his book on muscles and the heart. *De musculis et glandulis observationum specimen* – 'Anatomical observations on muscles and glands' – was published in both Amsterdam and Copenhagen in the course of the summer. It was dedicated to the King of Denmark-Norway, Frederick III. Stensen tried, in this way, to draw attention to himself personally and to the qualifications he had for a professorship in anatomy. However on the 29 August 1664, Matthias Jakobsen was appointed to the vacant position in geography, under the royal warrant. The best that could be said about him was that he was the nephew of

The treatise 'Muscles and glands' was published in 1664 and dedicated to King Fredrik III. The drawings in the four corners are a kind of contents list for the book. The two at the top show the muscles and the tongue, those at the bottom the lymph system and the umbilical sac in the egg. The drawings at the side of the title are, on the left, the heart seen from the side, and to the right a horizontal cross-section. The round figure immediately above the text is the heart's tip which shows the spiral structure of the muscles at this point. In the rich floral decoration, we find tulips, roses, aconites and hibiscus.

Thomas Bartholin. Biographers of Thomas Bartholin have described Matthias Jakobsen as the least suited to a professorship, of all the sons of Bartholin's sister. The vacant position in history went to Jakob Henrik Paulli who had already held a professorship in anatomy! It was not, therefore, by accident that a day later, on the 30 August, the royal exchequer made a joint payment of 300 riksdaler off the debt owed to Niels Stensen and Jakob Kitzerow. Posterity has with difficulty been able to interpret this as other than the payment of travel money for Niels Stensen.

There is no doubt that Niels Stensen suffered a grave injustice, as he was the obvious choice for a professorship in anatomy. How great an injustice can best be illustrated by a quotation from a respected history of Denmark (*Danmarks historie*, Politikkens Forlag, 1977).

> Thomas Bartholin praised the young genius to the skies – only to rule him out of court for the vacant professorship in anatomy. Seldom has such a great injustice been committed at the University of Copenhagen and seldom one that on the whole has had such serious consequences for Danish scholarship.

At the end of August 1664, Niels Stensen left Copenhagen. He must have felt rather depressed, after the death of both his parents and the shoddy treatment he had received at the hands of his Danish friends. There is no evidence that Stensen showed any signs of bitterness towards Simon Paulli and Thomas Bartholin who, together, had seen their mediocre relatives appointed at the University instead of him. Stensen was well aware how much they had helped him, through his school and university years, to become the man he was.

Others, however, have felt bitter, on his behalf, at the way he had been rejected by the University of Copenhagen. A. D. Jørgensen, in his biography of Stensen in 1884, wrote:

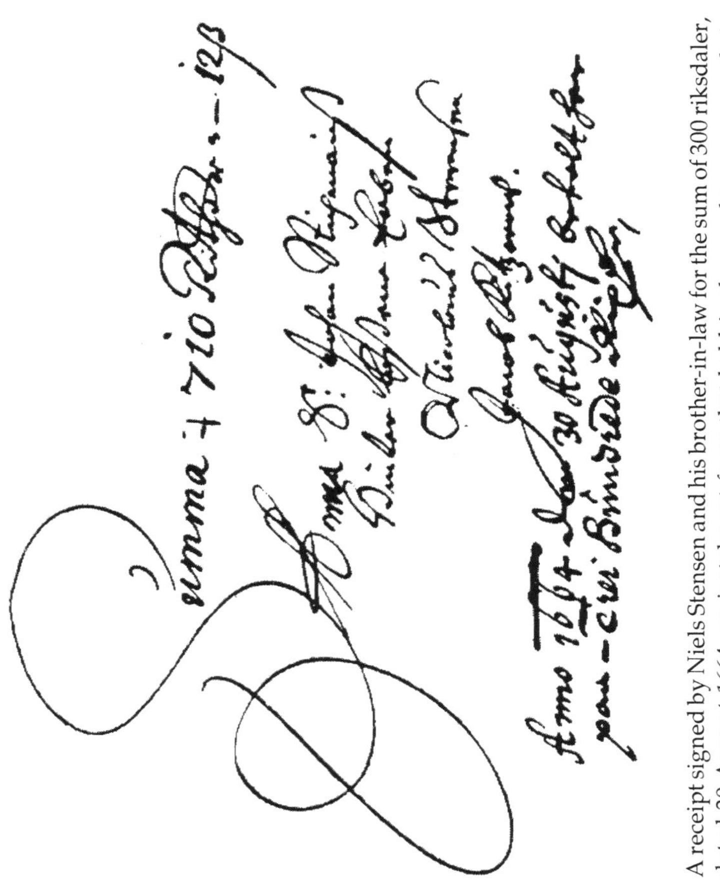

A receipt signed by Niels Stensen and his brother-in-law for the sum of 300 riksdaler, dated 30 August 1664, an instalment from that held in the royal treasury on their behalf.

> He had left the well worn path the craftsman follows [...] Through his intellectual brilliance he had broken into other social classes, which welcomed him with open arms so long as he remained a modest young student, but rejected him out of hand when his natural demands clashed with their privileges.

He was to go to Paris. We do not know the route he took apart from the fact that he stopped off in Cologne on the way. Once in Paris, the first thing he did was to send a letter to the University of Leiden asking to receive his medical doctorate without having to attend to defend it in person. The answer from Leiden University granting Stensen the degree in absentia is dated 4 December 1664 and reads:

> Dr Sylvius has informed the Senate that the very erudite young Niels Stensen, a Dane from Copenhagen, was examined last year by professors of the Medical Faculty, and that the examination showed he was wholly fitted, publicly and solemnly, to be awarded the highest medical award. Dr Sylvius furthermore declared that the same candidate had, on a previous occasion, delivered a public lecture for which he had received a glowing report. In his published thesis he had already displayed outstanding scholarship. He is now in Paris, and there are weighty reasons for his not being able to come to us, to deliver the required lecture and to request the degree. He therefore begs Senate to consider him worthy of the degree and to receive the title of doctor in his absence.
>
> When the Senate had heard the judgement of the Medical Faculty and the recommendations of the other professors, it decided, that this was a special case, and that this very learned young man should be awarded the degree he sought *in absentia*.[E 17]

In Paris, Stensen was the guest of the humanist Melchisédech Thévenot, a former French ambassador to the republic of Genoa, who later became librarian to Louis XIV. Thévenot was a rich man and provided financial support for many talented young scholars. One of these was Jan Swammerdam who had recently taken his doctorate at the University of Leiden on the topic of insect life. As the Sorbonne had not yet opened its doors to the natural sciences, it was in circles such as those formed by men like Thévenot, that they took root. Thévenot held weekly meetings in his home, where natural scientists, mathematicians and those with literary interests met, his house being the focus of a great deal of the academic life of Paris at that time. Later the group was to form the basis of the French Academy of Sciences which was set up in 1666. This was the Paris of Louis XIV to which people flocked from all over Europe. Moliére had already captured Paris with his satirically witty plays, which took issue with the hypocrisy and prejudices of the era. His encounter with France, his friendship with Thévenot and his intellectual milieu, were to be of the greatest importance for Stensen.

Stensen also became acquainted with members of Thévenot's family, and especially with his cousin Marie Perriquet with whom he had many conversations. She had belonged to the group attached to Pascal, who had died three years earlier. Stensen said that his acquaintance with this highly cultured lady was important for his understanding of the Catholic faith. Fourteen years later he was to write to Thévenot that: 'Among the people through whom God has shown his mercy to me [...] your position is assured, through the friendship you brought about between Miss Perriquet and I. That is why I include you every day in my prayers.'(E 146)

It is likely that Marie Perriquet introduced Stensen to the Danish-born Elizabeth von Rantzau, who was the prioress of a convent not far from Thévenot's house. She had, for a short time, been married to Josias von Rantzau who was a Marshall of France. They had both converted to Catholicism at a young age. He had died when Elizabeth was only twenty-three years old, and as they had had no children, she chose to enter a convent. Stensen had many conversations with her on matters of faith during the time he was in Paris, in which they discussed, amongst other things, the meaning of the Eucharist.

Throughout the summer, Stensen and Swammerdam lived in Thévenot's summer house at Issy. Often they went on field trips into the mountains to study rare insects and they also took time to examine the development of the chicken inside its egg. At the weekly meetings with Thévenot, Stensen gave several lectures. Stensen himself wrote little about his stay in Paris. What we know about him at this time comes from what others have written in private correspondence and from entries in Ole Borch's diary. It is clear that his was a name to be conjured with. From the magazine *Journal des Scavans* of 23 March 1665 we read of the young scholar, newly arrived in Paris:

> The Danish scholar daily undertakes dissection for the many that seek to increase their knowledge. He has also carried them out in the École de Médicine, where he has earned great admiration with his new discoveries. What is special about him is that he manages to make everything he undertakes so obvious, that one is bound to be convinced. It is remarkable that his findings have been overlooked by all previous anatomists.

What we know most about Stensen's time in Paris is undoubtedly his lecture on the anatomy of the brain which he probably gave at the beginning of 1665. The lecture was delivered in French and was described as an oratorical masterpiece in the Gallic mould, by the Frenchmen in his audience. It has subsequently been translated and published in many languages. Neurologists consider it a breakthrough in the understanding of the brain's anatomy.

Stensen moved from Paris to Montpellier around the middle of September 1665. He wanted to visit the famous medical faculty at the University. He met several English naturalists in Montpellier, men who were later to become members of the Royal Society in London. Among these were William Croone, John Ray and Martin Lister. They

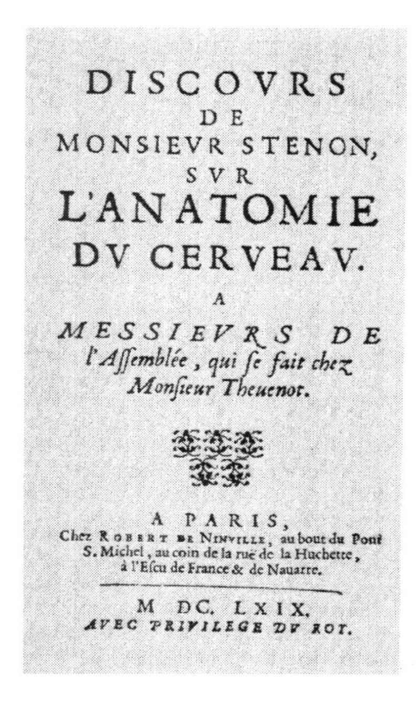

DISCOVRS
DE
MONSIEVR STENON,
SVR
L'ANATOMIE
DV CERVEAV.
A
MESSIEVRS DE
l'Assemblée, qui se fait chez
Monsieur Theuenot.

A PARIS,
Chez Robert de Ninville, au bout du Pont
S. Michel, au coin de la ruë de la Huchette,
à l'Escu de France & de Nauarre.

M. DC. LXIX.
AVEC PRIVILEGE DV ROY.

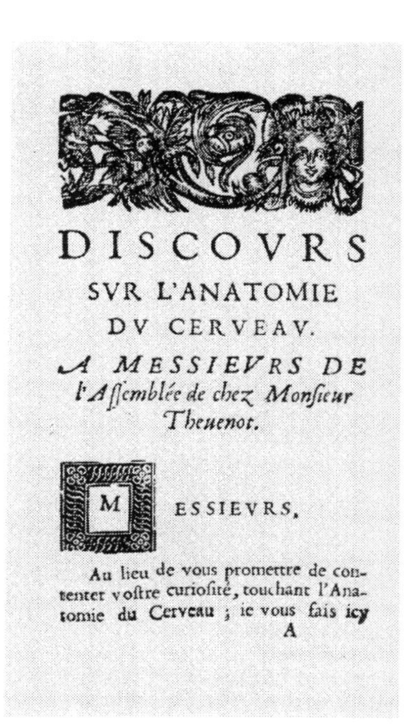

DISCOVRS
SVR L'ANATOMIE
DV CERVEAV.
A MESSIEVRS DE
l'Assemblée de chez Monsieur
Theuenot.

MESSIEVRS,

Au lieu de vous promettre de contenter vostre curiosité, touchant l'Anatomie du Cerveau ; ie vous fais icy
A

The title page and first page of Stensen's lecture on the anatomy of the brain which was published in French in 1669. The lecture had been delivered in Paris in 1665 for a group of scientists. Stensen set out the future direction of research on the anatomy of the brain.

were among the founders of systemic zoology. During the winter and summer of 1665–66, the four men spent a great deal of time together. There is no way of knowing precisely what topics they discussed, but one assumes that the origin of the earth and of fossils must have frequently been amongst them, for subsequently, Lister, Ray and Stensen all published important contributions towards the understanding of the earth's past. Thanks to his friendship with the three scientists, Stensen's academic works were quickly brought to the attention of the Royal Society in London and translated into English by able academics. Ray and Lister later cite Stensen's work, on geology and paleontology, on several occasions in their publications. Martin Lister, who was a doctor, mentions that once, in the course of the winter, he witnessed a dissection carried out by Stensen in the Earl of Aylesbury's study. He praises Stensen's genius and modest personality. Stensen knew many Englishmen, but never visited England.

In Catholic Italy

In March 1666, Stensen crossed over the Alps to Tuscany. Italy was a favoured destination for north Europeans and in the years 1536–1660 some 733 Danish and Norwegian students visited the country. At that time what is now Italy was divided into many small states of various sizes. Tuscany was one of them, lying in the middle of the long peninsula, with the Papal States to the east and south. Its northern neighbours were the two small states of Lucca and Modena. Tuscany had an area of over 12,000 km^2 and a population of around 700,000, with Florence as its capital. As a result of its size, the Pope had granted it the status of a Grand Duchy. The state was ruled by the Medici, a princely family that since the fifteenth century had made Florence a centre for art and learning, as well as a meeting place for all scholars visiting Italy. Leonardo da Vinci, Michelangelo and Galileo were all attached to

Florence and thanks to the support of the Medici family, had been able to develop their singular gifts. Stensen too was to enjoy the intellectual and financial support of the princely house. Without such favourable working conditions, it is unlikely that his academic enquiries in Tuscany would have been possible.

Stensen's first port of call was Pisa, where the Grand Duke Ferdinand II lived with his court. Letters of recommendation had already been sent by Thomas Bartholin and Thévenot to the Grand Duke, but they proved to be unnecessary, as Stensen's reputation as a scientist had already made him famous throughout Europe. He was warmly received by the Grand Duke who, together with his brother Leopold and several other spectators, wanted to observe his dissections. Prince Leopold of Medici had been a pupil of Galileo and was very interested in science. He is reckoned to be the most important of the seventeenth-century Medicis and in 1657 set up Europe's first experimental academy of sciences, *Academia del Cimento* or 'The Experimenters' Academy'. Its motto was 'Examine and examine again'. Its members usually met in the Medicis' palace in Florence, the Palazzo Pitti. The *Academia del Cimento* had a large collection of natural history objects, something that was unusual at that time. Here one tried with the help of a comprehensive exchange of correspondence with most of scholarly Europe to keep abreast with the latest developments in science and research.

Stensen was not long in Pisa before he continued on to Florence where he was well received by Leopold's librarian, Antonio Magliabechi. He had an unusually good memory and was known for being able to remember most of the content of the library's books. On this first occasion, Stensen did not stay for long in Florence as he wanted to visit Rome, which he had set as a goal for his journey to Italy.

He stayed in Rome for almost two months. He saw the huge new St Peter's church, which had been consecrated in 1626. During his visit, Stensen became acquainted with the well known French Jesuit and mathematician, Honoré Fabri and the Roman physicist, Michel Ricci. Both became aware that Stensen had little money left, and they wrote discrete letters of recommendation, touching on the problem, to Prince Leopold in Florence. Whilst in Rome, Stensen also visited the famous Marcello Malpighi, the founder of microscopic anatomy. He had, with the help of his microscope, discovered the circulation of the blood capillaries and the alveoli in the lungs.

On his journey back to Florence, Stensen travelled via the port of Livorno. He arrived on 24 June 1666, the day on which the Catholic Church celebrates the Feast of the Body of Christ (Corpus Christi). Stensen was amongst the spectators, in the Piazza Grande, of the solemn procession in which the monstrance[4] containing the host is borne around the streets of Livorno. The Catholic Church teaches that the host which is consecrated during the Communion service, is Christ's own body, and that those who take it, see and receive God himself. The teaching of the sacrament is inherently paradoxical, for at the same time as God in his incomprehensible might holds the world in his hand, he is wholly present in a little piece of bread. Stensen wrote of this experience:

> When I saw the host being carried in a procession through the streets, the following thoughts welled up inside me: either this host is a normal piece of bread and so those who accord it such honour are fools; or the host really does contain Christ's body and so why don't I too honour it? When this thought entered my head, I could not, on the one hand, conceive that Roman Catholics, who make up such a large part of Christendom and who count among them, so many intelligent and learned people, could be duped; and yet on the other hand I could not reject that belief in which I had been born and raised. And yet it was necessary to do one

---

[4] Derived from the Latin work *monstrare* – 'show forth'. An elaborate container in which the host is kept when it is set out for worship or borne in procession.

> thing or the other, because it was not possible to combine two such opposed propositions, or to regard a religion as true which, on such a central issue of the Christian faith, has lost the track and led its followers astray.[E 36]

In his conversations in Paris with Mademoiselle Perriquet and Elizabeth von Rantzau, Stensen had had explained to him the Catholic Church's teaching that Christ really was present in the consecrated host. When, in Livorno, he watched the procession and saw the believers kneel when Christ, in the form of a piece of bread, passed, this was for him evidence that Catholics took this teaching literally. Suddenly it became very important to him to discover whether the host was just a piece of bread or whether it really did contain the body of Christ.

When Stensen returned to Florence, the Grand Duke Leopold II appointed him anatomist at the Santa Maria Nuova hospital. In contemporary terms it was a thoroughly modern hospital with 1500 patients, several specialist departments and its own dissection rooms. Stensen quickly learned Italian and made many new friends, including the forty-year-old Francesco Redi – personal physician to the Grand Duke and a member of the *Academia del Cimento.* His specialist field of research was the poison of snakes and scorpions. Stensen also became acquainted with the somewhat older Vincenzo Viviani who was the Grand Duke's court mathematician and a leading engineer. He sought to determine the watershed between the rivers Tiber and Arno. Viviani had been Galileo's youngest pupil and was only twenty when the master died. In the last years of his life, Galileo was blind and Viviani took on the task of writing for him, including the manuscript of his last work on collision theory. Viviani was now engaged in writing a biography of the great natural scientist. Viviani was known as someone who easily fell out with people, but a close friendship developed between him and Stensen, who was younger by sixteen years. Someone else who came to mean a lot to

The Hospital of Santa Maria Nuova in Florence where Stensen was engaged as the anatomist by the Grand Duke of Tuscany in 1666. The hospital had room for 1500 patients and specialist departments for the injured, and for patients with gall stones, kidney stones etc., an epidemic section and an anatomy theatre.

Stensen was the Secretary of the *Academia del Cimento*, the twenty-nine-year-old Count Lorenzo Magalotti. He belonged to an old Roman aristocratic family and had had both Malpighi and Vivani as his teachers. Stensen soon found his place in this milieu that continued to work in the spirit of Galileo. According to his own testimony, his years in Florence were the happiest and most important of his life.

In 1666 Stensen finished his study *Elementorum Myologiæ Specimen* ('The characteristics of the muscle'). In this work Stensen showed, on the basis of geometical evidence, that a muscle's volume does not increase during contraction. The theory was not accepted at the time, in fact it met with a great deal of criticism. Only in our own times has its truth been established. The medical doctor Troels Kardel has devoted a lot of effort into getting Stensen's theory of the muscle accepted. In the 1990s the theory was finally confirmed with the use of modern computer technology.

Stensen lodged in a private house near the Porta Romania in Florence. The building no longer exists, but at that time lay not far from the Annalena convent, which ran a small shop selling herbal medicines, tea, essences, and hair oil. Stensen visited the shop occasionally and was often served by an elderly nun called Maria Flavia del Nero. Eventually, as they came to be better acquainted, they began to discuss matters of faith. When Stensen put a difficult theological question to her one day, she recommended that he should refer it to someone who was better informed than she was. Stensen felt unwilling to discuss Catholic doctrine with others; he admitted to her that he was too embarrassed and shy to discuss it with anyone but her. One morning, as they talked, the Angelus bell rang – the call to prayer in Catholic countries – and Maria Flavia proposed that they should recite the Angelus prayer together. Stensen went along with the first part of the prayer which consists of quotations from the Bible, but remained silent at the second part, in which Catholics pray that the Virgin Mary will intercede for them.

On another occasion she suggested that Stensen should visit the Church of Santissima Annunziata to look at the painting of the Annunciation of the Virgin Mary. Stensen visited the church later that same day and was gripped by its atmosphere, which inspired him to pray. According to Maria Flavia's memoirs, after that he often visited the church to pray.

Some fishermen caught an enormous shark in their nets off the coasts of Livorno. They killed it, brought it ashore and presented it to the Grand Duke who decided that Stensen should examine it. Stensen concentrated on the animal's head and found that its brain was small relative to the size of its body. He published his observations in a short treatise: *Canis Carchariae dissection Caput* – 'Dissection of a shark's head'. Leading zoologists who read the treatise today are surprised at how 'modern' it is, both in its language and reasoning. Towards the end of the dissection, Stensen examined the creature's mouth and saw the many rows of teeth that are a feature of sharks. He discovered a striking similarity between these teeth and the tongue-shaped stones found in Malta, which he had seen in Ole Worm's natural history collection in Copenhagen, during his student days.

Stensen was taken by the thought that the island of Malta had once been covered by sea and that the tongue-shaped stones could have been the remains of sharks which had lived in the sea there. He had earlier noticed that in Tuscany one found many stones that resembled the remains of creatures, especially mussels and snails. Viviani who, as a result of his many official visits, had a thorough knowledge of the Arno valley, gave Stensen good advice as to where to look for such stones. Stensen began a systematic search and concluded that stones that resembled parts of sea creatures were to be found in both hard and soft strata. He compared fossilized shells from mussels and snails with the shells of living creatures. The fossils must have been the remains of molluscs that had

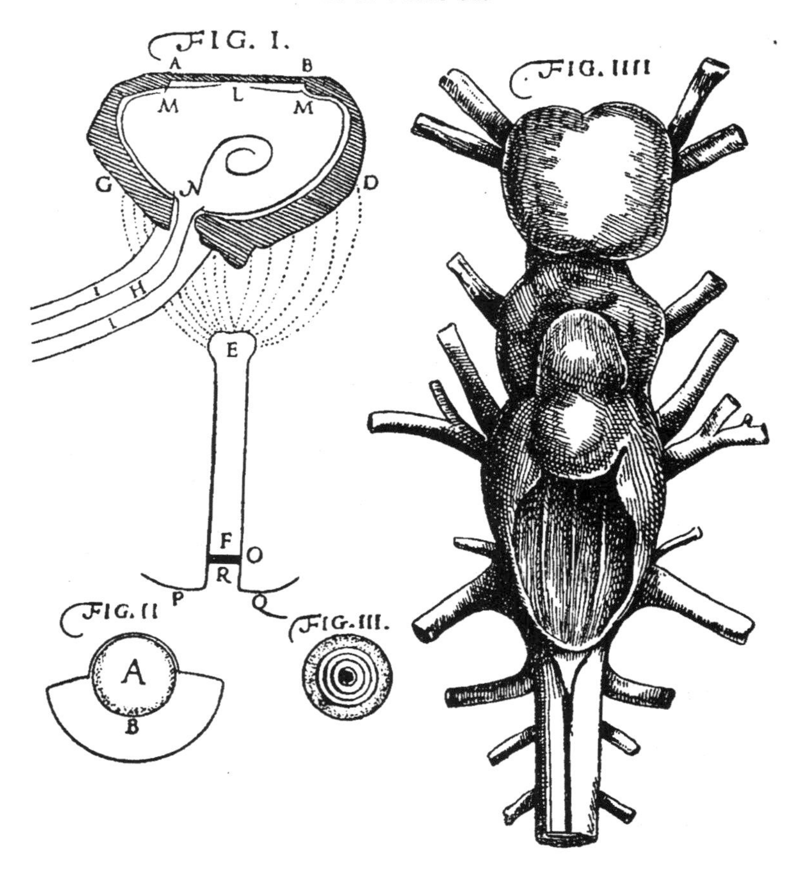

Stensen's own drawings of the eye and the brain from the great shark he dissected. (I) shows the shark's eye, where (AB) is the membrane that corresponds to the cornea (L), lens aperture (EF) a piece of the cartilage which provides support for the eye. (IHI) is the nerve of the eye, where (H) is the nerve and (I) the myelin sheath, (N) the place where the nerve enters the eye and makes contact with the light sensitive epithelium on the inside of the eye. (II) is the eye's lens. (III) shows the structure of the lens. (IIII) The shark's brains with its many nerves leading from it, the size of which are drawn with great accuracy. The shark weighed 1800 kg and the brain only about 93 grams. The drawing shows Stensen's skill as an illustrator and how he brought out the detail by the use of shading.

lived earlier, for their structures were the same. But how had they got into the stone? Stensen put forward the theory that the place where the fossils lay must, at one time, have been covered by sea. Dead creatures which fell to the bottom of the sea were, in the course of time, covered by mud from all the tiny particles which were deposited in the water and which eventually fell to the bottom.

Stensen was very taken by the phenomenon and continued his researches in different kinds of strata. The Tuscan landscape has a very varied geology that provided excellent opportunities for the study of the different ways a fossil can be formed.

When Stensen came to publish his book *On the characteristics of muscles* he included with it his essay on 'The dissection of a shark's head'. The Grand Duke paid all the costs associated with the publication. The Count spent that summer in Livorno and Stensen went there when he was finished with his treatise. He came to live in the same house as Viviani and the Grand Duke's personal physician Francesco Redi.

In one of the neighbouring states, Lucca, there lived a medical doctor who had some fossilized fish vertebrae from Malta that Stensen wished to see. Redi wrote a letter of introduction to the doctor about the north European who wanted to see the fossils. The day on which the visit was to take place happened to be a major festival in Lucca, so that Redi also wrote about Stensen's visit to Lady Lavinia Arnolfini. She was married to Lucca's ambassador to Florence and on the day of the festival was to be at her home in Lucca. Redi, who, in addition to his medical activities was also a poet, gave the letter a lyrical tone:

> A man born between the mountains of Denmark and Norway comes to see the most noble state of Lucca. He brings with him all that there is of chivalry and nobility in those distant lands, and if he had not had Luther's dogma drummed into

> him, I believe that your highness would judge him to be a person of unusual perfection. I recommend him to the influential protection of your highness, and his honour the Ambassador.

When the Grand Duke moved back to Florence for the winter, Viviani arranged for Stensen to have his own furnished apartment with a servant to look after it. It was but a short walk from his new home to the Annalena convent's shop, so one assumes Stensen must have told Maria Flavia about his visit to the Arnolfini family in Lucca. He did not know that the nun knew Lavinia Arnolfini. After the conversation, she wrote to Lady Arnolfini, and suggested that the ambassador's wife invite the young Scandanavian scientist who lived according to Luther's dogma. When the ambassador's family were again in Florence, Stensen often visited them and became close to the family. Lavinia Arnolfini had, when young, wanted to enter a convent, but following her parents' wishes, married an aristrocrat who was much older than her.

Stensen talked often with Lavinia Arnolfini about the Catholic faith. In the course of one of their conversations, she said to him: 'If my blood could help to convince you of God's truth, then in this instant would I give my life for your salvation.'

This conversation made a great impression on Stensen. Just as systematically as he had, time after time, researched new scientific topics, so now he began to study the original biblical texts and the Church Fathers' and Christendom's oldest texts, in order to arrive at a firm understanding of the true faith. From Maria Flavia's recollection of her conversations with the Jesuit Father Savignani, we know that Stensen had many acute objections to the concept of purgatory and the Pope's authority.

Geology and theology

Stensen continued with his geological investigations alongside his study of religious writings. That he was unable to free himself from his religious questionings is clear from a letter he later wrote to the philosopher and mathematician Gottfried Wilhelm Leibniz about his conversion:

> Either religion is a binding injunction which mankind concocted in order to show its Creator the adoration they owe him, in which case it is sufficient to follow the laws in the country one lives in; or else religion is prescribed by God himself and so there can only be one which must exist unbroken from the world's beginning to its end.[E 143]

His study of theological works and his conversations with Father Savignani and the two women, got Stensen to see the truth of the Catholic faith, but it did not bring about his conversion. Earlier he had been strongly influenced by Descartes' and Spinoza's view of religion. According to them, religion was a human expression of thanks to the maker. Therefore one religion could be just as good as another. The multitude of faiths in the Netherlands and the religious tolerance there, confirmed that. In addition, Stensen was aware that as a Catholic, he would not be able to get a post at the University of Copenhagen and would also anatagonize his family and friends in Denmark. On a later occasion Stensen was to write of this religious crisis:

> Even though I realised at once the reasons why I should submit myself, my mind was still so bound by the chains of darkness, torn by a variety of powerful concerns, that I barely had control over myself. I failed to find a way out of my unhappy predicament until one evening, on All Saints Day, so many proofs and so many differing circumstances presented themselves, that, at last, it was clear to me that God had taken me by the hand and led me to His church and that I must admit: 'Lord, you have freed me from my chains'.[E 73]

In November 1667, Stensen was received into the Catholic Church. He has written little about what got him to overcome his doubts and to convert to the Catholic faith. What he did write comes from a later date. In two letters to the Calvinist pastor Johannes Sylvius, written in 1670 and 1672, he touches upon this side of his conversion. The first of these ends with the words:

> Human proofs are to no purpose, if God's mercy is not upon one, so as to expose the errors of surviving opinions, to recognise the truth and to bind us to it. The divine assurance can only be understood by those who have experienced it. Praised be his name who led me from darkness into light, from death to life.[E 73]

It is not possible to explain adequately the 'change of heart' experienced by Stensen. Neither he himself nor others can, in words, explain why suddenly be should accept the 'divine truth', without further evidence or argument. His Italian friends knew a great deal about the Catholic faith, but had little experience of conversions. They didn't recognize that logical arguments and facts about the Catholic Church were not enough. Stensen himself was to convert many to the Catholic faith, for which his great knowledge of science and theology made him well suited. He never pressed anyone to convert, but convinced those who did, through argument and logic, of the truths of Catholicism. He stressed in several places that faith is a gift and he denounced forced conversions. He always left his converts to take the last step themselves.

At almost the same time as his conversion, Stensen received an official letter from the King of Denmark in which he was called home to take up a post in anatomy at the University of Copenhagen, with an annual salary of 400 riksdaler. But the offer was suspended, presumably because Copenhagen learned of his conversion.

Viviani wrote to Magalotti on 13 December that Stensen would not travel to Copenhagen before he knew how His

Majesty reacted to the fact that he was now a Catholic. As the King would probably not accept it, Viviani hoped that the Dane would remain in Florence.

It was not just Viviani and Magalotti who hoped to keep Stensen in Florence. Prince Leopold too wanted him to stay in Tuscany and take care of the *Academia del Cimento.* For the Prince had recently been appointed a cardinal and would, therefore, have little time to spare for the Academy. Early in 1668, Stensen carried out several investigations in the mountains of Tuscany, completing a series of drawings of the geological conditions there. In June 1668 he received a private letter from Denmark to the effect that there were now good prospects of his being called home in spite of his conversion. He could not, however, travel immediately as he had promised the Grand Duke that he would complete a major work on geology. The situation was such that he found himself extremely busy, writing up the notes of his investigations and completing the manuscript of his book. It was a rushed job, not, in fact, ever completed. Stensen gave it the Latin subtitle – *prodromus* or 'provisional'. The complete title was: *De Solido intra solidum naturaliter contento prodromus* – 'Provisional reports on solid bodies which are found naturally embedded in other solid bodies'. It is difficult to understand his haste, for he could presumably have been released from his promise to the Grand Duke and still travelled. For the news of the post in Copenhagen had come as a complete surprise. But Stensen did not like to leave loose ends and he had, perhaps, a presentiment that the future would not allow him to spend much time on geology. The work was dedicated to the Grand Duke Ferdinand. In the introduction Stensen explains its origins and mentions too his own situation:

> Since I have not accepted any request, I shall postpone my study until I have returned to my fatherland, in order to complete the work in all its detail there. Unless, that is, the same fate befalls me as in the past, namely that new tasks

> always prevent me completing the preceding ones. My enquiry into the marvellous structure of the heart stopped me from describing all the glands of the body. The death of my relatives stopped the investigations of the heart that I had already begun. So that I should not become too engrossed in an altogether too minute a description of the muscles, the seas which lap the shores of Your Majesty's country brought in a huge shark – and now, whilst I am engaged in my current enquiries, I am called away by the King of Denmark, whose summons, the law of nature and the great goodwill he has shown me and my family, I am bound to follow. What all this is due to I scarcely dare ask. Perhaps what I ascribe to myself should be ascribed to a higher power.

Once Stensen had completed the manuscript, he asked Viviani to arrange the practicalities to do with its publication. The manuscript had to be approved by the Inquisition before the Church would permit its publication. Viviani was nominated as the professional adviser. His judgement of the work was very positive.

Meanwhile Stensen awaited the official letter from the King, but it failed to arrive. He decided to travel anyway, reckoning that the letter would reach him in the course of his journey. He used the end of his stay in Italy to visit Rome and on his return north, again called into Florence. It was not easy to say goodbye to the friends who had meant so much to him. Many could not understand why he should leave the good life of Tuscany, where he enjoyed so many privileges, both at a personal level and in terms of his research.

Stensen left Florence at the beginning of November 1668. He first paid a visit to Malpighi in Bologna and from there crossed the Alps to Innsbruck where he called upon the Archduchess Anna de Medici of Austria, who was the sister of Ferdinand II. The Archduchess welcomed him with open arms and procured for him the most favourable conditions for studying mining in the area, and for undertaking anatomical investigations. Remembered from this visit is Stensen's dissection of a calf with a deformed head, which was painstakingly drawn with red chalk and given to the Archduchess, on his leaving Innsbruck.

Stensen continued on to Vienna and from there into Hungary and the mountainous areas of Slovakia, where, at that time, the most advanced mining of silver ore was to be found.

Following this diversion, Stensen travelled back to Vienna and then, via Prague, to Amsterdam, where he arrived towards the end of 1669. The letter from the King in Copenhagen had still not arrived so he used the time to look up his old acquaintances from his student days in the Netherlands. Jan Swammerdam had come back from Paris to his childhood home, the pharmacy in Amsterdam. Only here was he able to find sufficient peace to concentrate on his study of insect life.

In February 1670 Stensen, who was in Amsterdam, learned that King Frederick III was dead and that no letter offering a post in anatomy could be expected in the immediate future. Stensen could, therefore, allow himself extra time in the Netherlands before travelling back to Florence. His views on religious freedom in Amsterdam had changed in the seven years he had been away from the town. Earlier he had seen it as a release – now it appeared as a recipe for spiritual chaos. At a private party he discovered that the guests belonged to four different denominations. Several of his friends were searching in religious and moral matters, because so many religions and denominations were accorded equal status. We know that it was at this time that Stensen entered into a debate with the Calvinist pastor Johannes Sylvius. This was to continue by letter after Stensen had left Amsterdam. The contact with so many creeds and sects in the Netherlands which all claimed to be the truth, made a strong impression on him. It has been claimed that while his arrival in Amsterdam in his early years started his career as an anatomist, his later contact with the town as an adult was the beginning of his vocation to win souls for the Catholic faith.

His stay in Amsterdam came to an abrupt end when he learned that the Grand Duke Ferdinand was seriously ill and needed medical attention. Stensen travelled as quickly as possible back to Florence, but he arrived too late. Ferdinand II was already dead and had been succeeded by his son, Cosimo III.

The new Grand Duke gave Niels Stensen a hearty welcome and offered him the same pay and conditions he had enjoyed prior to his travels. In particular he asked him to arrange the mineral collection in the Palazzo Pitti.

Stensen started to catalogue all the mineral specimens belonging to the *Academia del Cimento* that were kept in the palace. One can still see today Stensen's characteristic handwriting on the labels attached to the specimens in the Palazzo Pitti. One also finds in the collection a piece of silver ore from Kongsberg, presumably a gift from the King of Denmark-Norway.

At the same time Stensen took up further work on his manuscript *De Solido,* with a view to a complete edition. His impressions from the Netherlands were still fresh in his mind and he wrote two long letters to Johannes Sylvius on why the Catholic faith was the true one. These were later published in book form with the titles: *On my conversion,* and *The defence of and further elucidation of the letter on my conversion.* Here he provides a wide-ranging justification for his conversion to Catholicism.

In 1670 there appeared an anonymous tract – a religious work called *Tractatus theologico – politicus.* The book which contained strong biblical criticism and a rejection of all miracles called for civil and religious freedom. When Stensen read it he realized that its author must be Spinoza. He wrote him a long letter in which he rejects the reforms which Spinoza believes are necessary to create a new philosophy, and urges him to examine the principles and teachings of Christian philosophy. He writes, amongst other things: '... and you will acknowledge, that the perfect Christian is the perfect philosopher whether it be an old woman or a servant girl who earns her living as a washer-woman'.

The letter shows Stensen's high regard for ordinary people – he ends it by expressing his willingness to examine, along with Spinoza, as many arguments as he would wish in order to cast light on the truth of the faith.

The royal anatomist

Towards the end of 1671, Stensen learned that the King wanted him to return to a position at the University of Copenhagen. It would appear likely that it was Peder Griffenfeld, the son of a neighbour in Klareboderne, who had persuaded Christian V to invite Stensen back to Denmark, and who had obtained for him the right to practice his religion. Peder Schumacker had risen rapidly in the world and was now the young King's most important advisor. He wanted, in some way or other, to attach his countryman, a genius in many people's eyes, to the University. The official invitation from the King reached Florence in April. The wording was broadly similar to that in the first letter from the King, but with the difference that Stensen was now granted religious freedom. Stensen answered yes immediately, travelled quickly northwards and reached Copenhagen on 3 July 1672.

Stensen moved in with his sister and brother-in-law who continued to live in Klareboderne. He looked up old friends from his student days and was able to take communion in the chapel of the French ambassador. The residence of the latter was not under Danish law, being seen as a little piece of France in the middle of Copenhagen. It was, therefore, possible to hold Catholic services there. The clergy in Florence had asked Stensen, once he was in Copenhagen, to keep a discreet watch on the situation of Catholics in Scandinavia and to report back. From those of his replies that have survived it would seem that,

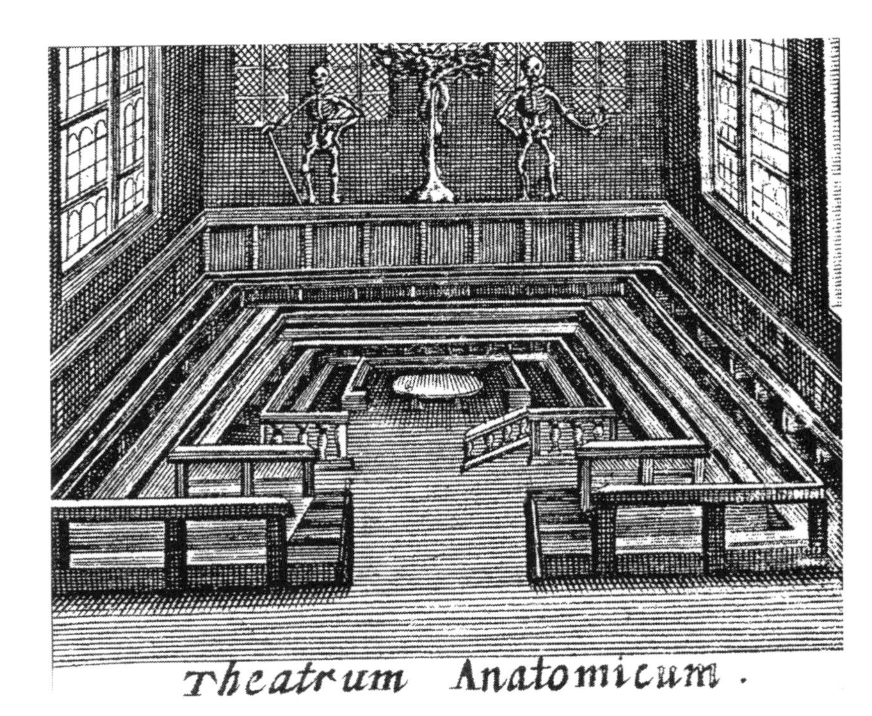

Theatrum Anatomicum – the anatomy theatre in Copenhagen where Stensen delivered his introductory lecture. There were two floors to the theatre with galleries and an auditorium. We see the dissection table in the middle and in the background two skeletons, Adam and Eve, by the side of the Tree of Knowledge and the Esculapian snake in stone.

from a Catholic point of view, the situation in Copenhagen was far from good.

In his letter of appointment from the King, Stensen was promised an annual salary of 400 riksdaler, but the precise nature of the post was not spelled out. He waited for a long time in the hope of getting some clarification and wrote about it to the Grand Duke Cosimo:

> As regards my post, nothing has yet been decided. The person who has undertaken the job of finding out what I can do is very busy.[E 82]

The person spoken of here was undoubtedly Griffenfeld, but Stensen dare not state this openly, as the letter could have been read by a third party and he did not want his childhood friend to be seen in a bad light by the Church authorities in Denmark. According to their law, university professors had to be members of the Lutheran Church and so there was to be no university post for Stensen in the two years he was in Copenhagen. It would have been possible to dispense with the law, but the opposition from the Church authorities was too strong. No one – not even Griffenfeld – dared to cross them.

Thomas Bartholin, in his journal *Acta medica et philosophica Hafniensa,* speaks of Stensen as the royal anatomist, but this was but an empty title. In reality it was only in a private capacity that he was able to undertake anatomical exercises. Bartholin was anxious to get as many academic articles as possible in his journal. Stensen was strongly encouraged to contribute and he did write a few minor pieces which were published while he was in Copenhagen.

At this time there was no anatomy teaching at the University of Copenhagen because there was no one qualified to undertake it. Only Ole Borch lectured 'on the human skeleton', and carried out some simple dissections of animals. Presumably it was Borch who had urged Griffenfeld to get Stensen to the University. When word got out that the famous anatomist had come to Copenhagen, the students came flocking. Holger Jacobæus and many of the younger generation attended Stensen's lectures and dissections. They were overwhelmed with admiration. At the beginning, Stensen dissected smaller animals in the summerhouse belonging to his brother-in-law Jakob Kitzerow. But when it came to larger animals, such as bears and reindeer, he used the anatomical theatre. Once he dissected a human, a soldier who had been hanged for theft.

Bartholin arranged for the first public dissection after the anatomy theatre had stood empty and dusty for many years. Now the King had chosen to reopen it and early in the year 1673, for a period of ten days, Stensen was able to undertake dissections in public. Bartholin, in his capacity as Dean of the Medical Faculty, sent out a formal prospectus, in which Stensen was described as 'the century's new Democritus'. The corpse of an executed woman was prepared for the occasion. On the first day, Stensen gave what has been called his introductory lecture. An extract from this is reproduced in the Catholic Prayer Book (1990) and reads:

> It is not the job of our senses to judge reality such as it actually exists, but to give reason a basis for judgement. In that way we are able to increase our knowledge so as to add to our insight.
>
> We have reason in order that we may evaluate the impressions of our senses. With the help of reason we can, through the impressions of our senses, raise ourselves to beyond the sensory. We must not, therefore, undervalue humanity and place it on the level of the beasts. On the contrary we must dwell constantly on and repeat to ourselves, this unalterable truth: we move from ignorance to understanding, from imperfection to perfection. Let us, therefore, cherish and cultivate such thoughts of humanity's worth that are worthy of humanity.
>
> When, then, each tiny particle of humanity's outward being is so beautiful and real for those who observe it, what beauty,

A statue of Niels Stensen clad in the typical attire of the baroque period. It was the work of the sculptor Gottfred Eickhoff and stands outside the main entrance to the medical and natural history section of Copenhagen's University Library. On the back of it is the inscription: *Anatomicus geologiae fundator servus dei* – 'anatomist, founder of geology, God's servant'.

what splendours, should we not see, if we could understand the structure of the entire body, if we could see the soul, which has so many incomprehensible instruments at its disposal, and if we could see how all this, of which we know nothing, depends upon a reason that comprehends everything.

That which we see is beautiful, that which we understand is even more beautiful, but the most beautiful of all is that which we cannot grasp. Let us not, therefore, be satisfied with the evidence of our senses, but through our bodily eyes, use our mind's eyes, as if they were windows in a glorious palace, surrounded by a beautiful landscape. Let us see what surroundings, what flowers, what elements and miracles are to be found.

For this is the purpose of anatomy: to lift the observer from the singularly brilliant construction of the body, to the dignity of the soul and from thence to acquire a knowledge and love for its Creator. The concern of anatomy is the body, and especially the human body, to the extent that we distinguish its individual parts and observe them by means of the senses. We cannot but be carried away by its overwhelming and discernible beauty. This makes us want to understand what we cannot grasp via the senses. When, through our intelligence, we observe the individual parts and compare them with each other, we are seized by the urge to investigate the source of all these miracles. Indeed, the greater the humility and the fewer the preconceptions we have, when we wander about in the vast forest of experience, the greater the understanding we acquire.

No sensible person can look at a statue, a painting, the movement of a clock, or a machine or any other ingenious artefact, without being seized by wonderment and admiration for its creator. How then can anyone who looks at the construction of the human body, which infinitely exceeds all that human ingenuity can produce, avoid being overcome by awe at and love for its Creator.

Yes, it is thus that God's singular providence has willed it, with that part of His creation to which he has given understanding. First, he pours over us, through the impressions of our senses all his treasures in a thousand different ways. Then he awakes in us a longing to explore the origin of these

> treasures. Finally he lets us find what we seek, so we recognise the giver by his gifts and can convey our love from the gifts to the giver.
>
> The anatomist cannot, therefore, take the credit either for his discoveries or the proof. The investigator is only God's instrument. God is not just content to contemplate his work, but is involved in carrying it out.

The speech has been reprinted on several occasions and in *Stenoniana* for 1933, Knud Larsen writes about its structure and choice of words:

> Structurally the speech is exceedingly elegant. Each section is harmonic, is built up logically and forms a natural bridge to the one that follows. The choice of words and phrases shows a great understanding for their musical qualities (*placuit deo ... placuit Regi ... placuit vobis. Demonstrandis ... monstrantis monstranda*. Unfortunately there is no way that a translation can reflect this.

For Stensen there was no conflict between faith and knowledge. For him they were but two sides of the same thing. The role of science was to provide insight into the beauty of the Creator's work and to generate love for Him. An echo of the same view is to be found in the work of the naturalist Linnaeus. He viewed nature as God's creation in which mankind was put on earth 'in order to extol and admire the unseen creator for his glorious work' (Kolsrud 1962). When Stensen gave this lecture he stood at the peak of his career as a scientist and had, with his exhaustive studies, witnessed the beauty of creation in its entirety. Stensen, however, does not confuse the issue, for after his lecture he devotes the next nine days to purely scientific matters. It is now the researcher who lectures by the side of the dissection table that bears the woman's corpse, and who concentrates totally on describing and explaining the anatomical structures that he reveals, bit by bit.

This was to be Stensen's only public appearance. The University failed to provide him with any further opportunities to dissect in front of large audiences. What should have been his inaugural lecture has, ironically, by posterity been characterized as his last. For the next eighteen months Stensen was a much sought after guest in Copenhagen's society, but this proved too much of a good thing. He quickly felt such sociability to be a pain.

Thomas Bartholin did much for public health. In addition to preparing a pharmacopoeia and a regulatory regime for the doctors of Denmark-Norway, he also saw through legislation requiring that midwives be examined. The first such examination took place on 30 September 1673 in the anatomy theatre. The fifteen candidates were examined by a panel consisting of Bartholin, Borch, Stensen, the royal physician Møinichen and the city physician Kölchen. The examination revealed that the midwives' knowledge of anatomy was pretty rudimentary. All were, therefore, ordered to follow Stensen's anatomical demonstrations for students during the coming winter. This was not, one can be sure, the kind of teaching the brilliant anatomist had reckoned on doing, when he travelled from Italy.

One of the Kitzerow family's friends was Johan Brunsmand, the headmaster of the Herlufsholm School. He was from Trondheim and had studied theology for a time at Uppsala before continuing his studies in Copenhagen. Brunsmand wanted to try to get Stensen back to the Lutheran faith, and to that end he translated a book that had been printed shortly after the Reformation. It dealt with an Italian lawyer who had become a Protestant, but who had abjured his new faith under pressure from the Inquisition. As a result he became deeply depressed. Brunsmand sent a copy of the book to Stensen. In his reply, Stensen thanked Brunsmand for the book but drew his attention to the fact that the doctrines which the main character in the book had been made to deny, were in reality those of Catholicism. The dispute between the two men was centred on their different views of the Church and the relationship between faith and deeds. The debate

Drawing of the University of Copenhagen in Frue Plads, as it appeared in the seventeenth century. The building to the left is the auditorium, in the centre is Domus Anatomica and on the right the dining rooms etc. In the background is Copenhagen Cathedral.

was hard fought and involved both speeches and writings. Brunsmand also tried personally to persuade Stensen, but even this failed.

Although Stensen had been granted religious freedom, he met opposition, both open and hidden, from many on the grounds of his faith.

Niels Stensen decided as early as 1674 that he would leave Copenhagen. Presumably his life in Denmark had become something of a backwater. He was not able to employ his outstanding talents and the tasks laid upon him were trifling in the extreme. His conditions of employment and his role remained unclear, and he had been subject to several attempts to get him to return to Protestantism. It must eventually have become clear to him that he would have to profess the Augsburg confession to be able to get a position at the University. The Grand Duke was aware of the situation and sent money to Stensen to pay for his journey back to Tuscany, once he realized that he longed to return.

Count Lortenzo Magalotti was at this time in Cologne, at a peace conference, and was intending to travel on to the court in Stockholm. On his way north he paid a visit to Copenhagen and implored Stensen to return to Florence as the Grand Duke Cosimo wanted him to be tutor to his son, the eleven-year-old Fernando. Stensen's letter of resignation was addressed to Griffenfeld, who, by this time was the country's Chancellor. Stensen's justification was that he had been invited back, by the Grand Duke, to bring up Tuscany's heir to the throne. Stensen also noted in his letter, that the last year had passed without his conducting any public demonstrations. His resignation was agreed on condition that he did not leave until he had been precisely two years in Copenhagen. As soon as the time was up he left the town at once. His salary for the second year was paid in arrears, but by then Stensen was already in Germany. He was in such a hurry that he didn't take time to wait for Count Magalotti who was still in Sweden.

The journey to Florence took longer than expected. Stensen paid a visit to Hanover where he met Duke Johan Frederick, who had converted to Catholicism after a visit to Assisi. The Duke was the brother of Frederick III's Queen Sofie Amalie. The Dukedom was Protestant, but the Duke had secured an agreement allowing him to hold Catholic services in his own castle. The Duke invited his guest to undertake some dissections while he was there. By way of thanks he gave money to Stensen and a large gold medal bearing his portrait. Stensen asked that a corresponding sum be given instead to the poor, and the Grand Duke agreed to this request.

Amongst Stensen's travelling companions were two young girls who had gone over to Catholicism in Copenhagen. Their conversion had led their families to wash their hands of them and Stensen tried to find a place that would take care of them. He succeeded in getting them into a convent at Hildesheim, where the prioress was Elizabeth von Rantzau, whom Stensen had known in Paris. In subsequent years he often found himself having to help Danish or Norwegian converts who suddenly found themselves alone in the world, or lost their posts as a result of their conversion. Legislation in 1643 had disinherited converts, something that brought many into serious financial difficulties.

The next stop was Cologne where a letter from Jan Swammerdam, inviting him to Amsterdam, awaited him. He had to change his proposed route in order to go there. His encounter with the town only served to strengthen his opinion of religious chaos that had gripped him three years earlier. Swammerdam had caught malaria which had led to a worsening of his depression. Stensen's friend had become obsessed by a religious sect which, in fact, was banned even in the Netherlands and which regarded all science as the work of Satan. At the behest of the sect, Swammerdam destroyed an unpublished work on bees, silkworms and May flies, which had taken a lot of hard work to complete. Stensen tried to get his friend to take up research again, but without success. Swammerdam later left the Netherlands to be with the sect on the island of Nordstrand in the Dukedom of Gottorp. After a time he returned to Amsterdam where he died a sick and broken man in 1680.

Priest in Florence – bishop in northern Germany

Stensen was not back in Florence until the turn of the year 1674–75. We do not know when he decided to become a priest, but it is generally thought that it was at about this time. Impressions from his time in Copenhagen and the sight of spiritual and material privation during his journey, brought fruition on the vocation he now felt. What had induced him to want to become a priest was checked thoroughly by Father Savignani and other clerics. They found him fit for the job, and because of his great knowledge, including theology, they decided that it would not be necessary for him to study that subject. Normally the Catholic Church demands several years of theological study before a candidate for the priesthood can be ordained. The Grand Duke released Stensen from his tutorial duties for a long period so that he could go on retreat and prepare himself spiritually for the priesthood. His ordination took place in Florence's Cathedral on Easter Eve 1675. In addition to the obligatory vows of obedience and celibacy Stensen also voluntarily took a vow of poverty. He now moved from the baroque upper class world of sumptuous excess to one of evangelical poverty, an ideal that was to be his object in life from now on. The day after – Easter Day – he celebrated his first Mass in the chapel of the church of Santissima Annunziata. The Danish philosopher Anton Thomsen wrote in 1910 that 'just as earlier in his science, Stensen had logically pursued his method until he reached to the bottom of a problem, now, with equal seriousness, he did likewise with Christianity'.

In May 1676 Stensen received a visit from three of his

former pupils in Copenhagen: Holger Jacobæus, Caspar and Christoffer Bartholin. Holger and Caspar were now professors and were making a study tour to Florence. Stensen welcomed his old students and helped them in all manner of ways during the six months they were in the city. Entries in the diaries of the three, and in that of Franscesco Redi, tell us that Stensen flourished as a priest. He had abandoned work on a major book on geology, but what he had written he gave to Holger Jacobæus so that he might complete it in Denmark. The manuscript never arrived – presumably lost during Jacobæus' journey home.

For almost two years Stensen worked, as tutor and priest, for the Grand Duke's son in Florence, his prime task being to teach him 'Christian philosophy'. In 1677 Duke John Frederick invited Stensen to Hanover in order to take over the vacant position of bishop in his dukedom, a choice that had the support of the papal delegate in Cologne. Stensen wanted to go, but had no desire to be a bishop. Eventually he was persuaded and after a lengthy period of preparation was consecrated a bishop in Rome in September 1677.

Shortly afterwards Stensen travelled north to Hanover. The Duke's estate lay in the Protestant part of Germany and the Catholic congregation was small, consisting, in the main, of foreigners. On the surface, at least, everything appeared to go well at this time, but Stensen missed the intensity of faith he had met with in Italy. There had been a rule in Hanover since the Reformation that no Catholic had the right to live in the town. However, a few years before Duke John Frederick had taken over the government of the territory, Catholic migrant workers had got permission to come to the town. Whilst in Hanover, Stensen wrote some minor theological works, including a defence of his conversion. He also conducted a lively debate with his opponents, in particular with Johan Sylvius in the Netherlands and the theology professor Kristian Nold in Copenhagen.

Stensen also entered into discussion of matters of faith

in Hanover itself. The Duke's librarian, the philosopher Gottfried Wilhelm von Leibniz, who was himself an evangelical Christian, had many conversations with the bishop on philosophical and theological questions. From surviving letters it appears that Leibniz tried to discover why Stensen had converted to Catholicism. Leibnitz was taken by the thought of a possible coming together of Protestants and Catholics. On one occasion he asked Stensen if he found the truth of the Catholic Church in 'the marrow of bones'. The two respected each other – both had great knowledge and were schooled in philosophy. Leibniz was also one of the few who understood the extent of Stensen's geological discoveries. An unknown manuscript by Leibniz was found in his archive in Hanover in 1996. It tells us that the author did not presume that fossils were organic matter but that they were created by the earth itself (Cohen, 1998). After Stensen's death, Leibniz tried to publish the manuscript which Holger Jacobæus had got for the proposed complete edition of *De Solido*.

John Frederick died in late 1679, to be succeeded by his Protestant brother. Catholic services in public were forbidden, and it was no longer possible for Stensen to function as a bishop. The Pope assigned him to the post of auxiliary to the Prince-Bishop Ferdinand von Fürstenberg in Münster. The latter was in poor health so that many of his management roles in the diocese were left to his auxiliary. Stensen had no previous experience as a church leader with many priests under him, so that he had to learn to be adaptable in relation to the priests for whom he was now responsible. His task was not made easier by the fact that the bishopric was poor and weighed down by debt from the Thirty Years War.

Stensen took his obligations as a bishop very seriously and during his time in Münster did his best to carry through a reform of the priesthood, for many priests were lacking in the education needed for their tasks and were negligent in fulfilling their obligations. His uncompromising stand regarding priestly conduct and the work ethic met with much opposition and hostility. However, Stensen's own example inspired many priests in the diocese to make a greater effort. As is often the case, Stensen's work was first appreciated after he had left the Dioceses of Münster and Paderborn.

Stensen's lifestyle provoked the chapter in Münster and eventually soured relations with it. A bishop who, during his visitations, walked round the diocese barefoot and who, as a whole, lived an extremely spartan existence, caused many an adverse reaction. Many were of the opinion that his ascetic lifestyle showed a disdain for the dignity of his rank. He neither dressed nor conducted himself in a manner that was fitting for a bishop. Most members of the chapter were engrossed in the financial benefits and other privileges that went with their posts and often neglected their pastoral duties. Stensen was especially angry over the way new posts were filled. Applicants often bribed those who made the appointments, in order to obtain a lucrative position. There was a tradition among many aristocratic families for sons to occupy particular church appointments for which, as children, they had been nominated. A system such as this, where the church was characterized by ruthless political power and abuse, was the exact opposite of what the new bishop wished, with his clear prioritization of pastoral tasks.

Relations with the bishop were, however, good and in his later years he always preferred Stensen to act for him, even though it would have been easy for him to get one of his many other assistants consecrated as a auxiliary.

When the bishop died in 1683, the chapter in Münster had to elect a new one. It was quickly apparent that the choice would be dictated more by financial and political motives than by any pastoral concerns. Stensen argued that the new bishop really must fulfil the duties of his position. The Cathedral chapter made a scandalous choice: the Archbishop of Cologne who was already bishop in three dioceses! This was the last straw for Stensen. He left

Münster saying he was making a visitation of an unknown duration. Instead he travelled to Hamburg where he lodged in the home of the Grand Duke Cosimo's ambassador, Theodor Kerckring, and wrote immediately to the Pope, complaining of the bishop's election. In his letter, Stensen pulled no punches in his criticism of conditions in Münster.

Kerckring, who was born in Hamburg, was an old student friend of Stensen and had converted to Catholicism during his time at university. On completing his studies he returned to Hamburg where he practised as a doctor. Hamburg, at this time, was almost completely Protestant and it was not possible to conduct services for the few Catholics living there. Stensen had, as early as 1681, had the idea of Kerckring being Tuscany's ambassador, were the post to be created in Hamburg. As the ambassador's residence would be regarded as part of Tuscany, a chapel could be created, so that Mass could be celebrated for the town's Catholics. Grand Duke Cosimo accepted the plan and a Tuscan embassy was set up in Hamburg. The Catholic congregation of the town numbered some 600 and was served by four Jesuits who lived outside it. There were a number of matters concerning both the clergy and the congregation that were deserving of criticism. Stensen tried to correct these, but he was strongly opposed and, in effect, prevented from carrying out any pastoral work in the town.

There were many poor people in Hamburg who received little attention from its rich citizens. Stensen devoted much time, and much of Grand Duke Cosimo's money, to help the many in dire need. The winter of 1683–84 was especially cold and Stensen's letters reflect the privations of the poor.

Stensen received a reply to his letter to the Pope in May 1684. In it he was reappointed as the Vicar Apostolic in northern Germany and Denmark-Norway. He decided to make a tour of the areas for which he was now responsible with a view to examining closely in each of them, the situation in which Catholics found themselves, and the possibilities for strengthening pastoral work amongst them.

In his private letters to the Grand Duke Cosimo from this period, it is clear that Stensen felt lonely as a priest in Protestant north Germany, where the impact of the religious wars was still clear. He was the only Catholic priest in Hamburg itself, where he felt his work produced little fruit. There is no doubt that he longed to be back in Florence and wanted to spend his last years there. The Grand Duke made clear in his replies to Stensen's letters that he would always be welcome in Tuscany. Stensen was of the opinion, however, that he could not return, but must fulfil the tasks which had been entrusted to him by helping the Catholics of northern Germany.

At the end of 1684 Stensen was visited in Hamburg by his sister Anne. She was passing through on her way back from France where she had been on a business trip for the goldsmith's workshop, which now provided a good income. Anne, who had recently been widowed, was relatively prosperous. The two liked each other and Anne undoubtedly had sympathy for her brother when she saw that he was ill and lived so very simply. But Anne turned a deaf ear when Niels began to speak of religion. She had been forewarned and justifiably so. Stensen had already brought one of her daughters and two of her nephews and nieces into the Catholic faith. Stensen's reasoning, and his ability to persuade in matters of faith, were legendary.

Stensen's last years

In 1684, Stensen had asked the Pope for two year's leave so that he might travel to Florence, take a holiday and undertake theological studies. The request was granted in 1685 and Stensen prepared to travel to Italy. But first he wanted to pay one last visit to Copenhagen. Christian V had issued a passport which his sister probably had with her when she visited him in Hamburg the year before. He was in Copenhagen for ten days in the autumn, living in the French Embassy.

Here he was able to celebrate Mass in the embassy chapel and in a room off the chapel he secretly confirmed some adult Catholics. Had that come to the ears of the Danish authorities, Stensen would have risked the death penalty. The law was pretty clear on this. '... I stayed ten days and celebrated the confirmation sacrament, which, as far as I am aware, has not been done since Luther's time,' he wrote from Hamburg to his superior in Rome.

Stensen visited those of his friends and relations who were still alive. Both Simon Paulli and Thomas Bartholin had died several years earlier. But he met his friend Ole Borch who was engaged in setting up a student hostel with the fortune he had amassed over the years. Borch's College was opened in 1691 and was, according to the statutes, to provide accommodation for sixteen Danish and Norwegian residents, of which ten were theologians. Stensen also visited Caspar Bartholin and Holger Jacobæus who still had good memories of their study tour to Florence. When he left Copenhagen, Stensen carried a letter from these two to Magliabechi, the Grand Duke's librarian in Florence.

After he had taken his leave of those closest to him in Copenhagen, Stensen lost no time in setting off for Italy. He took a mail coach, the fastest means of travel at that time, and after five days he was in Hamburg again. Here he found a letter awaited him from Christian Ludvig of Mecklenburg, in which he offered to buy a house specifically for Stensen in Schwerin, which could be furnished as a presbytery. He also gave Stensen permission to conduct services in the castle's chapel. Stensen had, for a long time, sought to get the Duke to create a chapel in Schwerin, as he saw it as a base on which to build missionary activities in the area. The letter from the Duke was therefore encouraging. After some consideration, Stensen chose to give up his trip to Italy. He would stay in northern Germany in order to exploit the possibility that had so suddenly been opened up for him. To have a priest living in his own house would provide a rallying point for the Catholic congregation, which numbered only eighty. Stensen decided to travel to Schwerin in order to bring the 'mission station' into being.

In the Middle Ages, Schwerin was the seat of a Catholic bishop, but after the Reformation the population was reduced to some 2,000. The Duke, Christian Ludwig, had converted to Catholicism in Paris, where he lived for most of the year. The court's chaplain at the palace, Father Jakob Steffani, was an arthritic old man and the only Catholic priest for miles around. Steffani wrote to Duke Christian Ludvig in Paris that Bishop Stensen was a holy man whose life was exemplary and that many attended the chapel whenever he preached in French and German. As Father Steffani was ill, Stensen, for all practical purposes took on the role of a parish priest for the tiny congregation in Schwerin. He had often to travel long distances to outlying places in order to visit sick and dying Catholics. It was tiring work which sapped his energy, even though he enjoyed working as an ordinary priest. Nevertheless it is clear from his correspondence of this period that he felt pretty lonely as a Catholic priest in a Protestant environment, and he longed to be back in Tuscany with the human support he could get there. Duke Christian Ludvig, who never appeared during the year Stensen was in Schwerin, provided neither moral nor monetary support.

In March 1686 Stensen was offered the post of auxiliary bishop in Trier. His renown as a saver of souls and restorer of church life had led him to be sought after for this position. Stensen was again in two minds over this and wrote to Rome for advice. Father Steffani had recently died and there was no possibility that the congregation would get a new priest in the first instance. There were, therefore, good grounds for Stensen to stay where he was. At the same time he recognized that his hopes of establishing a mission station with its own church was not a realistic proposition, under prevailing conditions. The congregation was too small and the opposition of the Protestant population too great. He had followed his calling but had seen no results. In the meantime he continued his work in the congregation. Many who came into contact with him converted to the Catholic faith, whilst the attitude of a number of Protestants towards this ascetic priest had changed. All the same the situation was hopeless. On top of this he suffered from kidney stones and in November 1686 had an attack of colic. He was in pain but, nonetheless, carried out his daily duties. A surgeon was brought, but he could do nothing. The next day his stomach swelled enormously and he suffered great pain. Stensen was now aware that his end was near. He asked that a message be sent to a Catholic priest in Lübeck, and that he be given pen and ink so that he could write his last will and testament. He wrote to Kerckring in Hamburg to arrange some financial matters and managed to complete a farewell letter to the Grand Duke Cosimo. In this he made three requests: that Cosimo would pay his debts of 300 *daler*, take care of the converts who lived with him, and pay for his burial. He also managed to finish a letter to his sister Anne. His stomach continued to swell and the course of the night he burst out: 'Surely I can swell no more?' and immediately afterwards he begged:

> 'My God I am in great pain. My God I beg you not to take the pains from me, but to give me patience to bear them. If we have taken the good from your hands, why should we not also take the evil? Either you want me to live or do die: your will be done'.

The priest from Lübeck did not arrive and throughout the night Stensen continued to proclaim: 'Jesus, my Saviour.' The priest had still not arrived on the morning of Thursday 25 November 1686. Stensen realized that he would not have the opportunity to confess his sins before he died. He asked, therefore, that those who were present would hear his public confession. Those who were with him said the prayers for the sick, but as the end neared, he said: 'Dear friends, you must say the prayers for the dying'. He died shortly afterwards. He was forty-eight years old.

Stensen's coffin was placed in the crypt of the palace chapel. Stensen had long since sold his bishop's robes, his bishop's cross and staff, and given the proceeds to the poor. A priest was sent for from Hamburg to come with the bishop's vestment to clothe the corpse. After the funeral service the coffin was transferred to Schwerin's Lutheran cathedral where it was displayed until the following March. Theodor Kerckring wrote to the Grand Duke Cosimo that Stensen had a great reputation for his holiness, not only amongst Catholics, but also amongst Protestants. Cosimo grieved inconsolably over Stensen's death and asked Kerckring to send the corpse to Livorno. Kerckring wrapped the body in cloths that had been moistened with spiced fluids to reduce the smell and rate of decay, put it in a box labelled 'books'– and sent it by boat to Livorno. Most ships' captains are not happy to sail with a corpse in the hold!

The following year Stensen was buried in the crypt of the Medici's own church, San Lorenzo in Florence. His last resting place was to be in the town that had given him the happiest moments and where he had his closest friends and benefactors.

As part of the canonization process, Niels Stensen's grave was opened in 1953 and the coffin taken to the chapel in the church itself. An antique marble sarcophagus, donated by the Italian government, was placed above it. The chapel was given the name Cappella Stenoniana. When Stensen was declared holy, the Pope said of him:

> Niels Stensen was a great scientist and bishop. He was always convinced that nature bears testimony to God's existence. But most of all Stensen sought the ultimate cause God himself, who cannot be found by the measuring instruments of science, but who can only be approached through the intu-

The sarcophagus of Niels Stensen in the Capella Stenoniana of the San Lorenzo church in Florence. The sarcophagus is decorated with flowers and wreaths for the 300th anniversary of his death in 1986. The marble epitaph on the wall was presented by delegates to the Second Geological Congress held in Bologna in 1882. The inscription pays homage to Stensen as the founder of geology. (Photograph K. Kluge)

ition of the heart. He was God's devoted servant and he teaches us that the world in all its beauty is not a goal in itself. He exhorts us all to appreciate God's glory and to recognize our dignity as human beings. (Kuhne, 1989)

Pioneering Anatomist

In the course of his career as an anatomist, Niels Stensen made some great discoveries that paved the way for others. These have been described, in several books and essays about him, as the result of his having amazing powers of intuition. Before the 'Chaos' manuscript was discovered in 1946, some of Stensen's biographers had doubts as to whether he had read much of significance in contemporary anatomical literature, during his years at university. Now that the whole of the 'Chaos' manuscript has been analysed in detail, the exact opposite is thought to be the case. Indeed he is today credited with being all but a genius while still a student. However, there were no signs of this either in his childhood or in his early years at university.

Stensen spent much of his childhood and adolescence in the goldsmith's workshop, where he watched how his father, and later his step-father, formed and shaped often tiny objects from precious metal. From an early age he learned to observe and to see the significance of even the smallest item for the overall effect. At the same time he must have realized that without an overall plan, there was little point in being painstakingly precise with the individual parts. Success depends upon bringing together the parts and the whole. What was to characterize his work as a scientist was his ability, at one and the same time, to have an eye for the detail and to place it within the wider context.

Not all first attempts are successful, a satisfactory result emerging only after repetition. The master craftsman is a master primarily because he has had a great deal of practice in what he does. A beautiful piece of jewellery is the product of many small steps, some forward, some back. There is nothing either remarkable or clever about someone who enjoys such experiences early in life. But there is no doubt that having had such experiences was a definite advantage for Stensen when he came to learn how to dissect. To master the art of dissection requires at least as much practice, precision, and sharp sightedness as the work carried out in a goldsmith's workshop.

What is unusual about Stensen are the conclusions he drew, as a scientist, from his observations. Care and clarity of thought, helped him to move towards an understanding of an organ's function and operation. Many contemporary and earlier anatomists had made the same observations as Stensen, but in the areas he researched, only he understood the structures and their significance for the living organism.

To understand how an organ functions demands a fundamental understanding of the entire organism in which it finds itself. Stensen had the necessary academic background thanks to the sound teaching he had enjoyed during his university years. His teachers in Copenhagen, Amsterdam and Leiden were amongst the finest of their time. Thomas Bartholin, Blasius, Sylvius and van Horne were all famous as a result of their anatomical discoveries. Stensen's director of studies was Thomas Bartholin who kept a close eye on him throughout his studies. Even when Copenhagen was besieged, the University closed, and contact with Bartholin severed, Stensen was helped to continue his studies. Ole Borch, Stensen's old teacher from the Latin School, a qualified physician and well trained in other sciences, gave him valuable advice as to which books he ought to read. Both Simon Paulli himself and his extensive library must also have been a very important source of knowledge for Stensen during his university years.

Ductus Stenonianus

At the age of twenty-two Stensen made his first important anatomical discovery whilst living with Blasius in Amsterdam. Of the dispute between the two men as to who had made the discovery, Stensen was to write to Bartholin in 1661:

> It is now a year since I was a guest of Blasius. During the lecture course delivered by Blasius – it ended three weeks after my arrival – I got hold of some anatomical specimens and asked the famous man if I might do some dissection work on my own. After getting his permission, I had a remarkable stroke of luck. For in the first sheep's head I bought and dissected myself I found a passage which, so far as I was aware, no-one had previously described. At first I thought I would dissect the brain and so I'd removed the outer tissue when suddenly I got the idea of first examining the ducts which ran through the mouth. I, therefore, conducted a probe through the tissue in order to examine the course of the veins and arteries. Suddenly I discovered that the tip of the probe was no longer pressed between the different membranes, but was moving freely inside a capacious cavity. When I pushed the probe further down I could hear that it was coming up against the teeth. I was surprised at this and asked my host for his opinion. He at first accused me of having created the passage by pushing too hard with the probe. Later he thought the phenomenon was a caprice of nature and referred me to Wharton's book, although even there he was unable to find a description of any such passage.[E 1]

In 1656 the Englishman Thomas Wharton had published a book on glands which, at the time, was considered the standard work. Wharton believed that saliva was secreted from the saliva glands that lie at the root of the tongue. According to Wharton the parotid gland consisted of porous tissue which collected excess fluid from the veins in the head and returned it to the venous system. If we accept Wharton's reasoning we would not expect to find any passage of the parotid gland to the oral cavity. We cannot, therefore, blame Blasius for first thinking that it was a question of shoddy dissection work. His pupil had only just arrived and could be considered a novice in the art of dissection.

A few days later, Stensen of his own accord, carried out a new dissection – this time of a dog's head. He found the same duct. On arriving at Leiden, Stensen mentioned his discovery to Professor François de la Boë Sylvius in the context of the latter's teaching of anatomy. Sylvius quickly succeeded in detecting the duct of the parotid gland in different animals and in humans. Professor Jan van Horne gave a demonstration of the discovery in the course of a lecture and named the duct, *ductus stenonianus*. The duct continues to bear that name, although, unfortunately, not without a long dispute over who had first discovered it.

New views on glands

Inspired by his first discovery, Stensen continued to carry out dissections. It was not long before he discovered that the inside of the eyelid was covered by many minute tear glands. From closer study he understood that the lachrymal fluid was secreted from the tear glands, and that the function of the fluid was to reduce the friction between eyelid and cornea. Contemporary anatomists believed that tears were produced by the brain and were carried to the eye via the veins. It was thought that the nerves were hollow, whilst the physiological function of the lachrymal fluid was still unknown. Stensen also discovered how the excess fluid was carried away from the eye by lachrymal ducts. The tiny ducts found in each eyelid, run into the corner of the eye and carry the lachrymal fluid, via the lachrymatory bag, to the nasal cavity. The ducts were known by contemporary anatomists, but none understood their role.

Stensen was the first to understand thoroughly the role of the glands. In many cases the task of glandular secretions is to ensure a frictionless movement between different tissues in the organism. He wrote in an essay that 'the most ingenious of mechanics' lubricates the eye with tears just like an ordinary mechanic lubricates an axle with oil.

Stensen was taken by the thought that wherever moisture exists on the human body it must be the result of glandular secretions. He began, therefore, to look for glands on those parts of the body which are normally moist. This led him to discover previously unknown glands. By studying corpses, Stensen was able to see with the naked eye the tiny sweat glands and the ducts that emerge all over the body. He discovered the glands in the mucous membrane of the nostril, but was unable to explain their role, which is to supply moisture to the inhaled air.

He discovered that the auditory canal contains ear wax glands, that the palate has several saliva glands, and that in the oesophagus are glands with ducts through the cartilaginous tissue.

Stensen also dissected fish. Here he established that the mucus of a fish is a glandular secretion. Many of the glands he described are so tiny that they are on the edge of what can be seen with the naked eye.

Stensen's discoveries were published in a book entitled *Observations on muscles and glands*. It marked a breakthrough in the understanding of the structure and function of glands. The book describes, for the first time, that the role of a gland is to secrete a fluid, the secretion, which has a physiological significance. It is therefore, understandable that the author describes the glands as 'the Creator's most sublime creation' and regrets that anatomists had paid so little attention to them. The book's discoveries were accepted relatively quickly by Stensen's contemporaries and made him a famous man. This was well merited for he had, in fact, mapped out most of the organism's exocrine glands which furnish secretions to the skin or the body's cavities, and, in most cases had also explained their specific role. The endocrine glands which

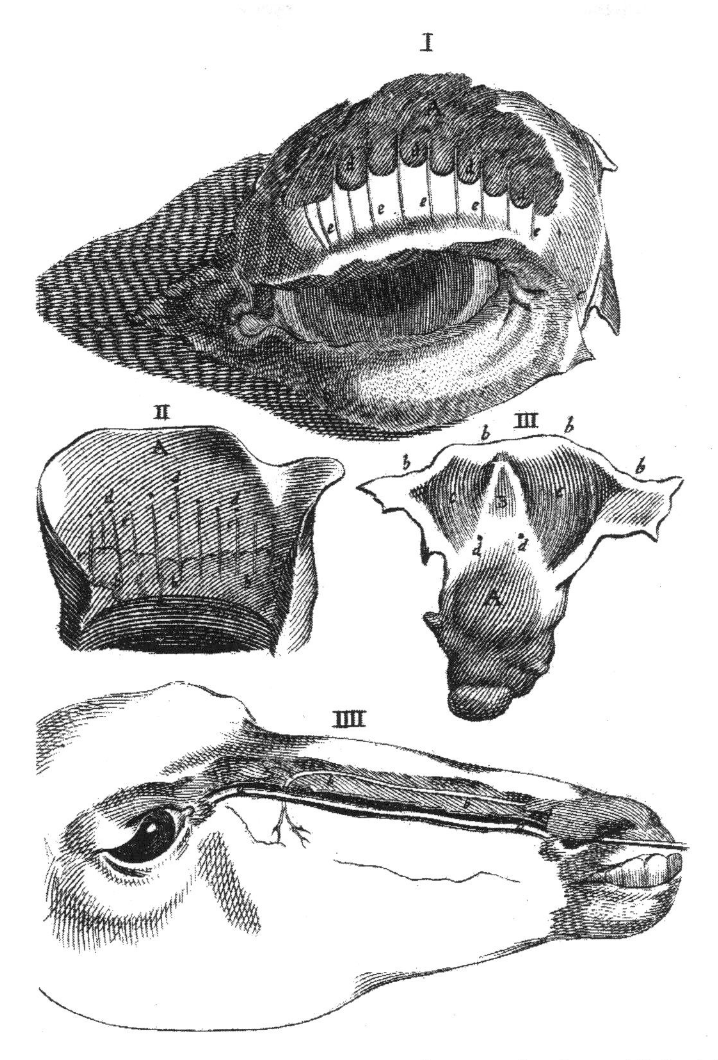

Stensen's illustrations in his treatise on the tear glands, published in 1662. (I) shows the left eye of a calf with the tear gland (A) with the parallel row of ducts (e) revealed. (II) shows the back of the upper eyelid with the tear gland (b), its ducts (c) and openings (d). The eyelid is turned upside down. (III) shows the tear gland and its two ducts in the corner of the eye. (IIII) shows the lachrymal duct (a) which takes excess tears from the eye to the nasal cavity. The long duct from the cheek to the nose is marked (b).

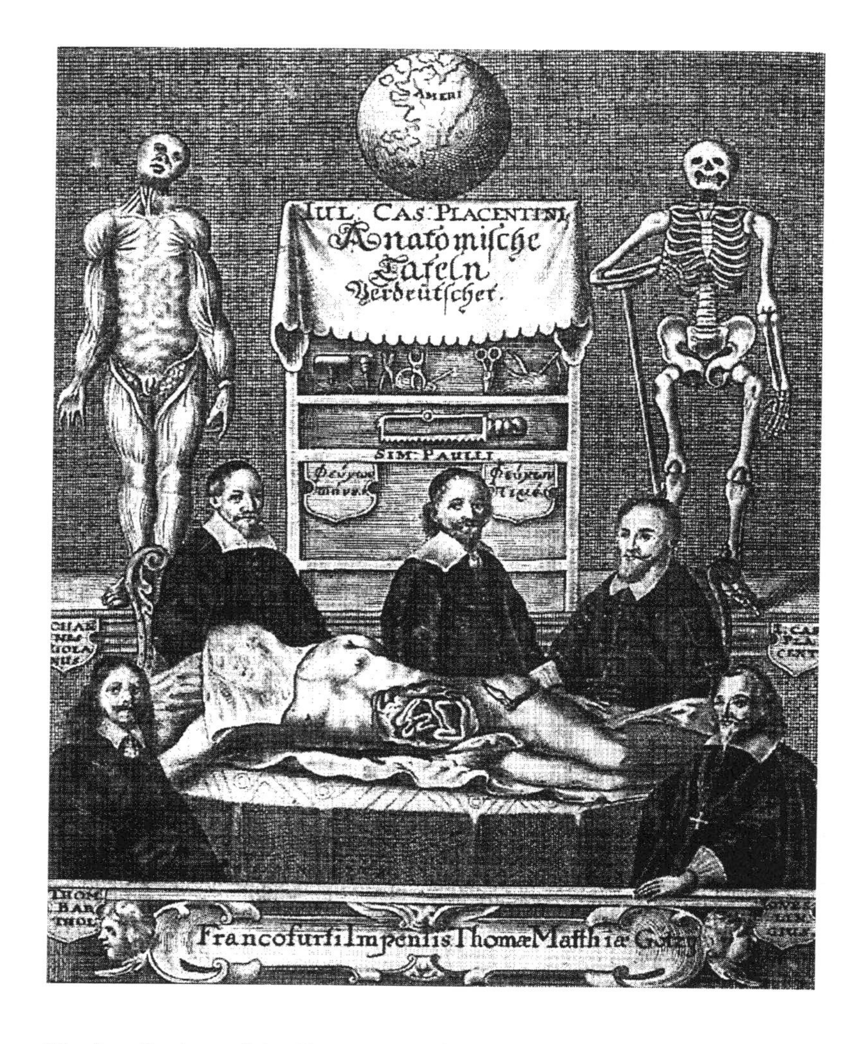

The frontispiece of the German translation of Casserios' *Anatomic plates* published in Venice in 1627. In the middle is Simon Paulli, the translator of the work. To his left is Riolan, his old teacher, and on the extreme left is Thomas Bartholin. On the right of Paulli is the author of the book, Guidio Casserio, and on the extreme right Johannes Vesling, his successor at the University of Padua.

do not have ducts and which secrete the products directly into the bloodstream were, with the exception of the pancreas,[5] not known in those days. Not until 1902 did Ernest Henry Starling describe the function of secretine,[6] and reveal the physiological significance of hormones.

The heart and the circulation

The English doctor, William Harvey had, in 1628, described the pumping function of the heart and the passage of blood through the arteries and veins. His experimental proofs opened a new epoch in science. Harvey also launched the theory that all life came from an egg and so refuted the theory that it could occur on its own. In 1661 Malpighi proved, with the help of a microscope, that a network of capillaries (the smallest blood vessels in the circulation system) join the arterioles and venules. Stensen had read these works and used them in his anatomical work. In 1662 he carried out the vivisection of a raven, studied the heartbeat and saw how the heart was filled with venous blood from the *vena cava* (the great vein in the thorax), from which it was pumped out via the pulmonary artery. Afterwards he tried to see what would happen when he stopped parts of the blood's circulation. In his essay on the dissection of a shark's head he mentions a comparable exercise carried out on a dog:

> I have observed that a ligature placed on the aorta, the latter not having been perforated, stopped all movement in the lower parts, every time I tightened it, with movement returning each time I loosened the ligature. I demonstrated this several years ago in Florence, where the dog survived the experiment, without any restriction on its freedom of movement, once the ligature was removed. As there still remain

---

[5] The Barvarian doctor J. G. Wirsung, detected the pancreatic duct in 1643.

[6] Secretine is a hormone which is formed in the duodenum and is important for digestion.

> some untested methods as regards the carrying out of the experiment, I won't say anymore about it.

The experiment has been given the name of 'Steno's experiment'. The *aorta descendens* is that part of the aorta which carries blood to the organs and which lies below the heart. With this experiment, Stensen had shown that the function of the muscle was dependent on its blood supply. Research members of the Royal Society tried to repeat the experiment but without success, because they perforated the aorta. When the ligature was loosened, the blood flowed out of the organism, instead of to those organs that lay below the heart.

In a letter to Leibnitz, dated 1677, Stensen describes how, whilst studying in Leiden he dissected the boiled heart of an animal:

> A Swedish friend once brought me the lungs of an ox with the heart still attached, so that I could examine the properties of the lungs. Having finished with the lungs, I boiled the heart to see if it was muscular or not. And the first fibres of the heart that I touched after cooking it and removing the membrane, led me to the lowest pointed part and from that upwards, so that the entire structure of the heart was revealed. [...] Shortly afterwards I made a comparison of the heart's structure with that of the muscles. I took the foot of a rabbit, which I'd already dissected – and the first muscle I worked on revealed, with the first incision, the structure of the muscle in a way that had not been known previously.[E 143]

Hippocrates had asserted, in the days of ancient Greece, that the heart was a muscle, and William Harvey cited him on this in 1628. But he had not stated his reasons for believing it to be so. No one in Stensen's time took the assertion seriously. The heart was thought to be the home of the soul, the centre of vitality. It was generally thought that the heart was a mystically superior organ that warmed the entire body, like the sun sending out its rays. Neither Descartes nor Harvey had entirely rid themselves of these notions about the heart. To say that the heart was a muscle and nothing more, was completely unheard of. The earlier notions have persisted down to our own times. We still depict the heart as the source of love and warmth, even though most of us know that it is a pump which, under certain circumstances, can be replaced. Both Hippocrates and Harvey had said that the heart was a muscle, but neither had been able to prove it. Stensen had boiled a heart and found a structure like that of muscles. But he had yet to prove that the heart's more fibrous structure was the same as that of other muscles.

The contraction of muscles

He began, therefore, to investigate muscular tissue in many parts of the organism. He found muscles in the temple, the diaphragm, the oesophagus, and discovered that the tongue consisted of muscles – something not previously known. Stensen published his findings in *De musculis et glandulis observationum specimen* (Observations on muscles and glands). He explains at length the structure of muscles and tells how the contractions take place in the muscle's fibres and not, as previously thought in the sinews. The study of muscle structure showed that the more fibrous structure of the heart was nevertheless the same as the other muscles he had examined. He concluded, therefore, that the heart was a muscle. 'Yes, truly, the heart is a muscle' he exclaimed, as a sort of affirmation of Hippocrates and William Harvey. He continued:

> The heart cannot, therefore, be a special substance, not the seat of heat, of innate warmth, of the soul. It cannot even produce its own fluid as blood, nor can it bring forth spirits, as for example the vital spirit.

Had Stensen's contemporaries accepted this theory, then many opinions as to the organism's function would have to be abandoned. As a result his discovery was not generally accepted.

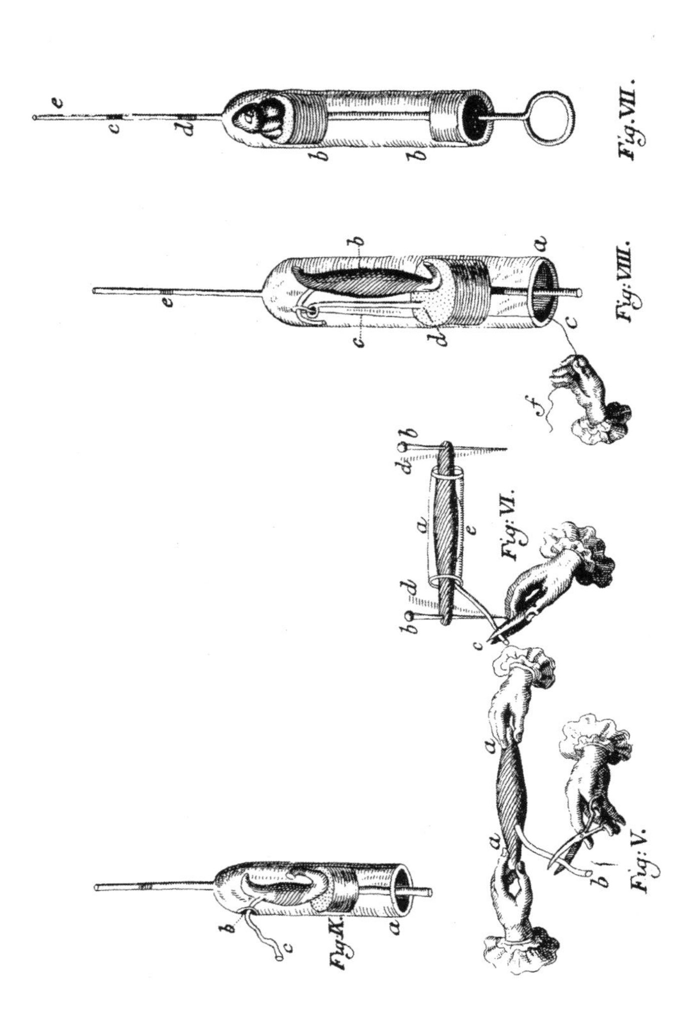

Jan Swammerdam showed from experiments that he carried out in 1660 that the muscles of frogs did not change in volume, even if they swelled up and became thicker by contraction. A drop placed in the mouth by a syringe where the muscle is placed, remained stationary when the muscle was stimulated to contract. Published for the first time in Leiden in 1737.

Stensen continued his study of muscles after arriving in Tuscany. He was able to establish, on the basis of geometrical calculations, that the volume of a muscle does not increase when it contracts. He was able to confirm this experimentally with the stretched muscle of a frog in a closed container, an experiment he carried out with Jan Swammerdam. Stensen published his theory of muscle contraction in his *Elementorum Myolgiae Specimen* – 'On elements of myology'. The theory aroused much criticism, one of the strongest critics being Giovanni Borelli, Professor of Mathematics at the University of Pisa, a member of the Accademia del Cimento and thirty years older than Stensen. He was of the opinion that a muscle's volume increased when it contracted. Stensen's writings on the muscle have been little read or cited, and previous biographers have spoken of them as, perhaps, the least significant of his academic output. It wasn't, and still isn't easy to determine the correctness of Stensen's theory, and, as a result, it has not been accepted. One reason for this is that researchers have directed their attention towards describing and explaining the contraction of the individual fibres of the muscle, whilst Stensen's theory says something about the muscle as a whole, which, in addition to the muscle fibre, is made up of sheets of connective tissue joined by tendons.

As recently as the 1990s, researchers created computer programmes that simulate what happens when an entire muscle contracts. The results have shown that Stensen's theory is correct so that now, more than 300 years since it was first propounded, it is at last generally accepted.

New insights into brain research

Niels Stensen did not himself publish anything on the anatomy of the human brain. That he is honoured today for his contribution to the understanding of that organ is due, above all, to his famous lecture on the brain, which he

NICOLAI STENONIS
ELEMENTORVM
MYOLOGIÆ SPECIMEN,
SEV
Muſculi deſcriptio Geometrica.
CVI ACCEDVNT
CANIS CARCHARIÆ DISSECTVM CAPVT,
ET
DISSECTVS PISCIS EX CANVM GENERE.
A D
SERENISSIMVM
FERDINANDVM II.
MAGNVM ETRVRIÆ DVCEM.

F L O R E N T I Æ,
Ex Typographia ſub ſigno STELLÆ. MDCLXVII.
Superiorum Permiſſu.

Frontispiece of the book which contained the three treatises covering the main work on the muscles, the dissection of a shark's head and an examination of a smaller shark. Published in Florence in 1667.

delivered in Paris in 1665. Others took care of the manuscript and published it, for the first time, in French in 1669. The lecture consists of four parts:

1. An admission of how little was known about the brain.
2. An account of the usual sources of error in brain research.
3. The need for new techniques in the study of the brain.
4. A new agenda for brain research and a re-appraisal of accepted views on the organ.

Stensen began his lecture by demonstrating how little was known about the brain:

> Gentlemen!
> Instead of promising to satisfy your curiosity as to the anatomy of the brain, I must admit to you, in all honesty, that I know nothing about it. I would wish, wholeheartedly, that I was the only one who had to admit this, for then I could, in time, derive benefit from the knowledge of others. It would be a great blessing for mankind if this organ, which is the most cleverly constructed of all and which is often attacked by serious diseases, was as well understood as many philosophers and anatomists imagine it to be.

He examines the different parts of the brain, describes the white and grey matter and regrets that so little work has been done on the former. He goes on to speak of the ventricles in the brain and argues strongly against the contemporary view that the individual ventricles were, respectively, the seat of understanding, judgement and memory.

> The ancients have been on the wrong track, as regards the ventricles, when they assumed that those at the front are the seat of understanding, those at the back, of judgement. They did so because they believed the power of judgement, being

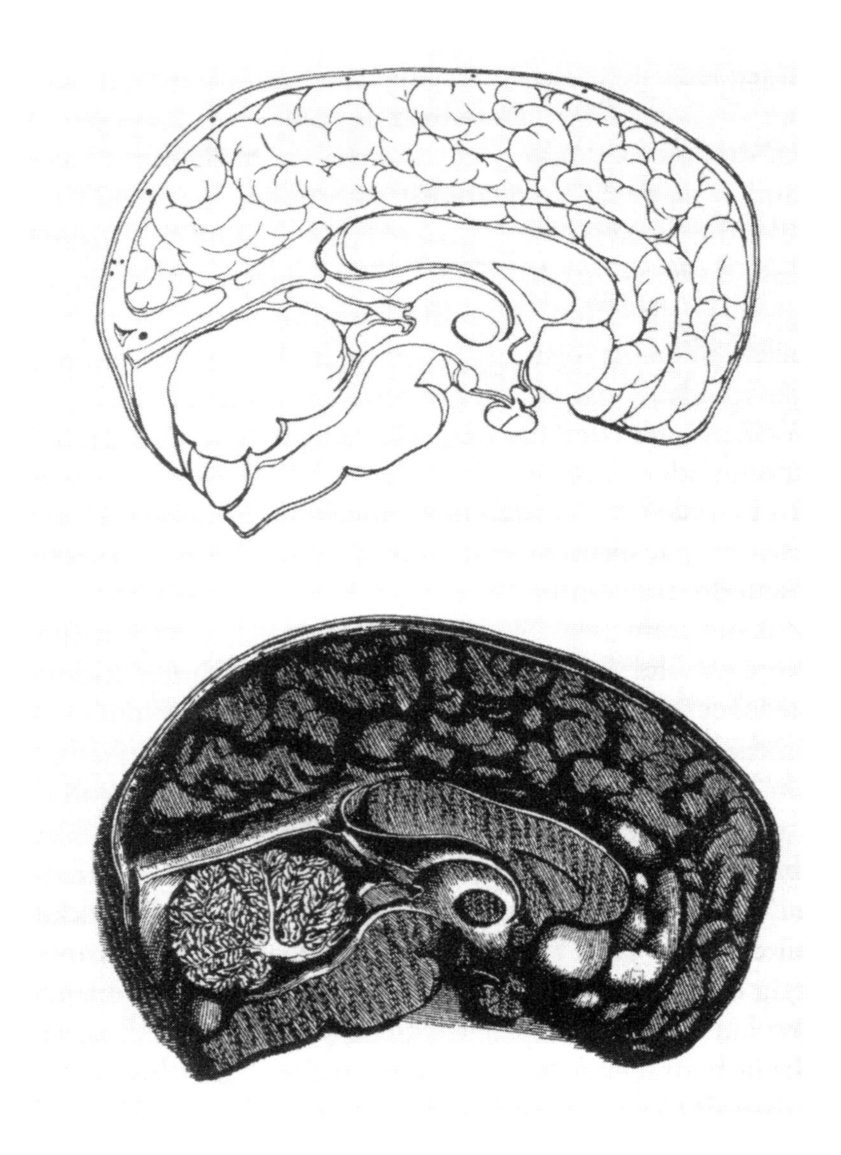

One of the plates with the cross section of the human brain used by Stensen in his lecture in Paris in 1665.

> in the middle ventricle, could the more easily process ideas which came to it, now from the one, now from the other ventricle. We can but ask those who go along with the views of the Ancients to give us grounds for believing them. I can assure you that of all the grounds that have been advanced in favour of this view, not a single one is convincing.

Stensen pointed out in his lecture that in the act of dissection we affect the objects we are investigating. What we see when we mount an organism for dissection can be very different from the condition of the living organism. This is an important factor that we must be aware of both when dissecting and making preparations to do so. Many observations of biological structures both before and since, have been misinterpreted, because these conditions have not been taken into account.

> Since dissections and preparations are subject to many errors and because anatomists, right down to our own times, have been far too uncritical in allowing themselves to construct systems and then fitted the soft parts to them, it is no surprise that the diagrams that have been drawn are inaccurate. It is not just an incompetent piece of dissection that is the cause of inaccuracy, but the incompetence of the draftsmen also plays a role.

Later in the lecture he continues:

> You have now seen, gentlemen, in what way the dissection of the brain has been carried out up to now and how little enlightenment we have gained from it, as well as how unreliable a picture the diagrams give of the parts they purport to represent. On the basis of this, you can judge what confidence you can have in the explanations that rest on such unsure foundations.

Stensen criticizes the absolute certainty displayed by contemporary anatomists and philosophers, regarding the structure and function of the brain. He rejects Descartes' notion that the pineal body, *glandular pinealis*, was the link between the body and the soul, on the basis that:

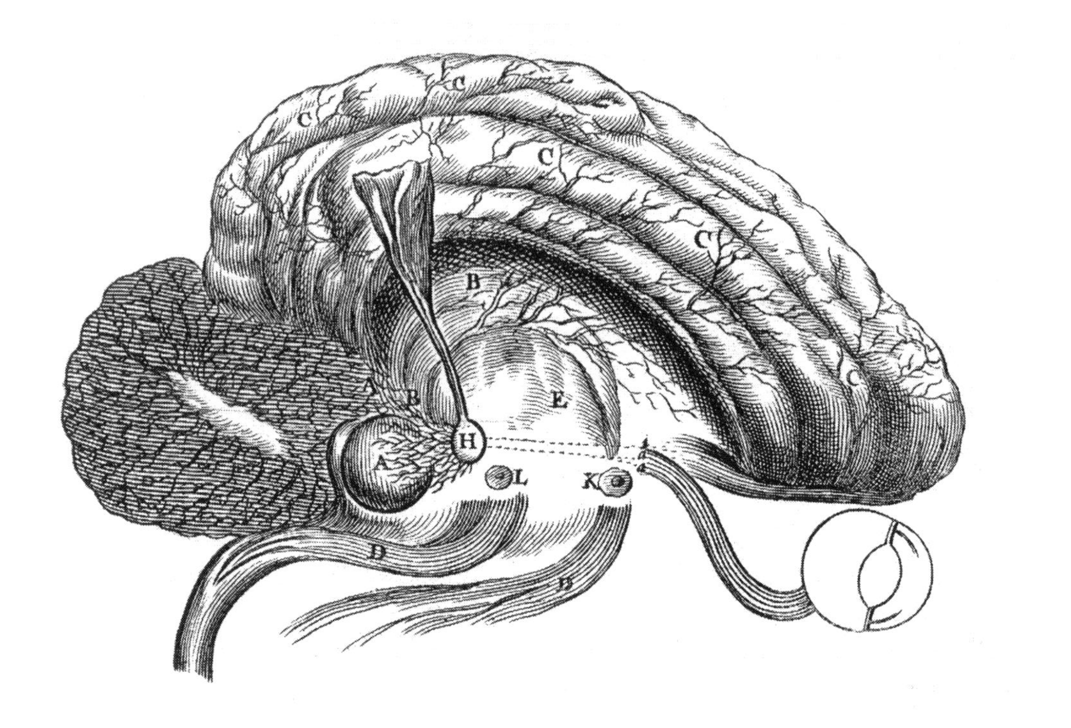

Descartes book *On mankind* was published in 1662, long after his death. This illustration of the brain is taken from the book and shows the pineal body (A) drawn excessively large.

> As regards what Descartes says about the pineal body's influence on actions, that at times it inclines to one side or the other, experience teaches us that it is no position to do this. The [pineal] body is so hemmed in by all parts of the brain and so attached to them on all sides, that it would be impossible for it to execute the slightest movement without doing damage to them and without severing the ties which hold it firmly in position. As regards its position it is easy to demonstrate the opposite of what Descartes teaches, since it is located not perpendicular to the brain, nor is it inclined forwards, as many of the most able anatomists believe, rather its tip is always turned towards the cerebellum, the little brain, creating an angle to the base of approximately 45°.
>
> That the [pineal] body is connected to the brain with the aid of arteries is not correct, for the circumference of the base of the [pineal] body is attached to the substance of the brain, or better still, the substance of the [pineal] body is located in the brain, which is the exact opposite of what Descartes asserts.

Stensen concludes his lecture by calling for a collective scientific effort instead of a blind belief in the authorities. He recommends that wholly accurate drawings of the brain be made and that its different parts be given unambiguous anatomical designations.

The lecture is unique in that it – to use a modern expression – represents a paradigm shift in brain research. Contemporary anatomists were confronted with how little they actually knew about the brain. At the same time, Stensen demonstrated that progress would only be made if painstaking investigations and a precise terminology replaced speculation and theorizing. Stensen's lecture contained few answers, but he posed the right questions. That is still today an important pre-condition for progress in research.

On this Stensen says:

> There are only two ways we can learn to understand a machine. The first is by the master who built it showing us how it was made. The second is to strip it down to its

> smallest parts and then to investigate each on its own and then in relation to each other. These are the proper ways of learning about a machine's construction. Nevertheless most have believed that they can get better results through proceeding by conjecture, and that it was not necessary to investigate at close quarters, with the aid of the senses, in order to understand it.

Stensen's lecture on the brain was translated into Latin and English shortly after it was delivered. For many years afterwards it was to be found in anatomical textbooks. On several occasions neurologists and natural scientists have caused it to be reprinted and interpreted. For the most recent reprint, which appeared in 1997, Troels Kardel provided both a commentary and computerized graphics of the brain.

Other anatomical discoveries

Anatomists in Stensen's time were both aware of the ovaries and the fallopian tubes and of their function for oviparous animals. The corresponding organs of mammals and humans had also been described, but were understood to be rudimentary testicles, *testes mulierum* – 'the female testicles'. When Stensen dissected a sea cat, *Scyllium canicula,* he found it had female reproductive organs similar to those found in hens and other birds. It was the first time this had been pointed out for non-oviparous creatures. Later he studied the organs of birds, frogs, various mammals and humans. By comparing his observations he was able to show that the organs of reptiles, mammals and humans were analagous, and ought to have a common designation, namely the ovary and the fallopian tubes.

After publishing his discoveries in 1667, Stensen continued his investigations of the female reproductive organs. The results were first made public in 1675, three years after van Horne, Swammerdam and de Graaf had

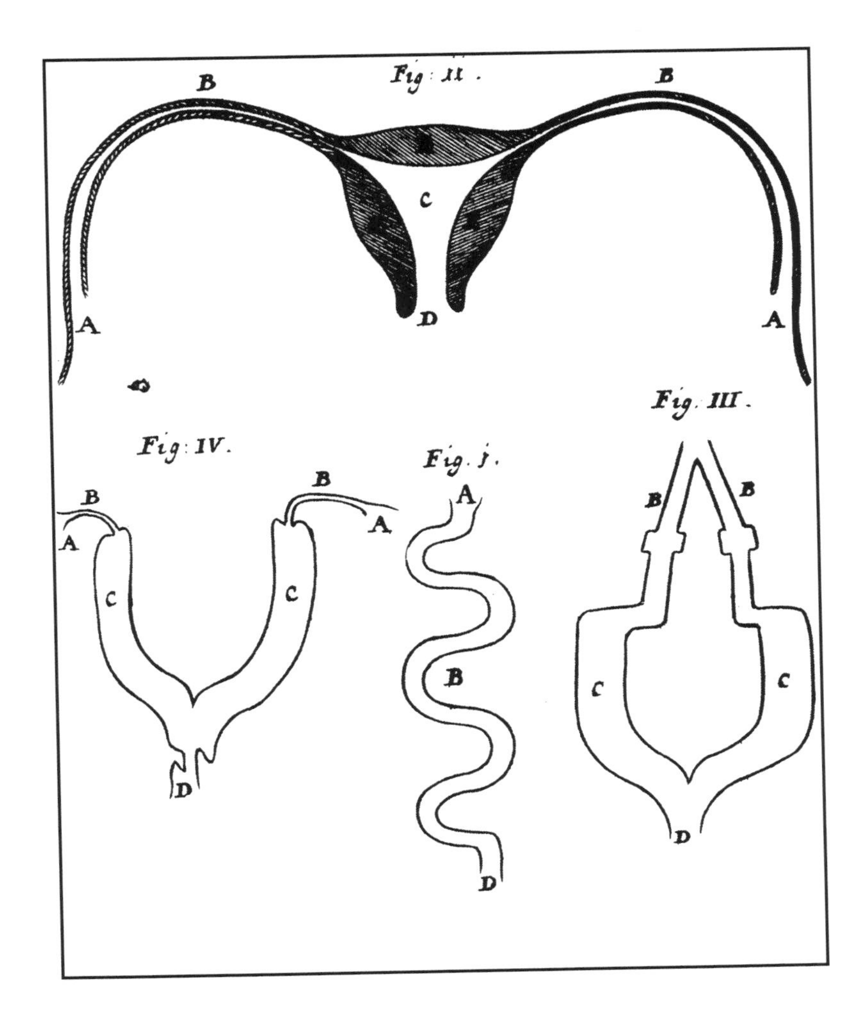

Figures from Stensen's article in the journal *Acta Medica & Philosophica Hafniensia* (1673) with the female sex organs from (I) a hen, (II) a woman, (III) a shark and (IV) a wolf. One assumed that the organs of humans and mammals were rudimentary testicles, but through his comparative studies Stensen showed that they were ovaries and Fallopian tubes.

published an essay on the ovaries. Swammerdam and de Graaf came into bitter conflict over who had first described the ovary's follicles in humans. The Royal Society in London had to make a judgement on the issue and decided that neither of the two had made the discovery. That honour fell to Stensen. However this is the organ that continues to this day to bear the name of Graaf's follicle.

When Stensen was in Paris he performed an autopsy on a stillborn child with heart disease. He was the first to describe this abnormality. Two hundred years later, in 1888, the French physician, Arthur Fallot, observed the same deformity – it is one of the most common congenital heart conditions, with a blue tinge of the skin and mucous membrane. The re-discovery led to its being given the name *Steno-Fallot's tetralogy*. The word tetralogy indicates that the condition involves four malformations of the heart which occur together. The first is an opening in the inter-ventricular septum (i.e. the partition between the right and left ventricles); the second is a narrowing of the pulmonary artery; the third is a displacement of the aorta to the right so that it, in part, emerges from the right ventricle and, in part, from the left; and, the fourth, a thickening of the wall of the right ventricle. The deformity is a very serious one, and the blue colour, which leads to children suffering the condition being called 'blue babies', is a sign that the blood contains too little oxygen. Previously 'blue babies' died before reaching adulthood, but today the condition can, in many cases, be rectified by surgical intervention.

Stensen discovered that milk production was a result of glandular activity in the breast. Previously it had been thought that milk had been produced elsewhere in the body and carried to the nipple in special vessels. Stensen wrote about his observations in a letter to Thomas Bartholin dated 5 March 1663:

> Many had thought they could see ducts carrying milk from internal ducts up to the nipples, but so far as I am aware they

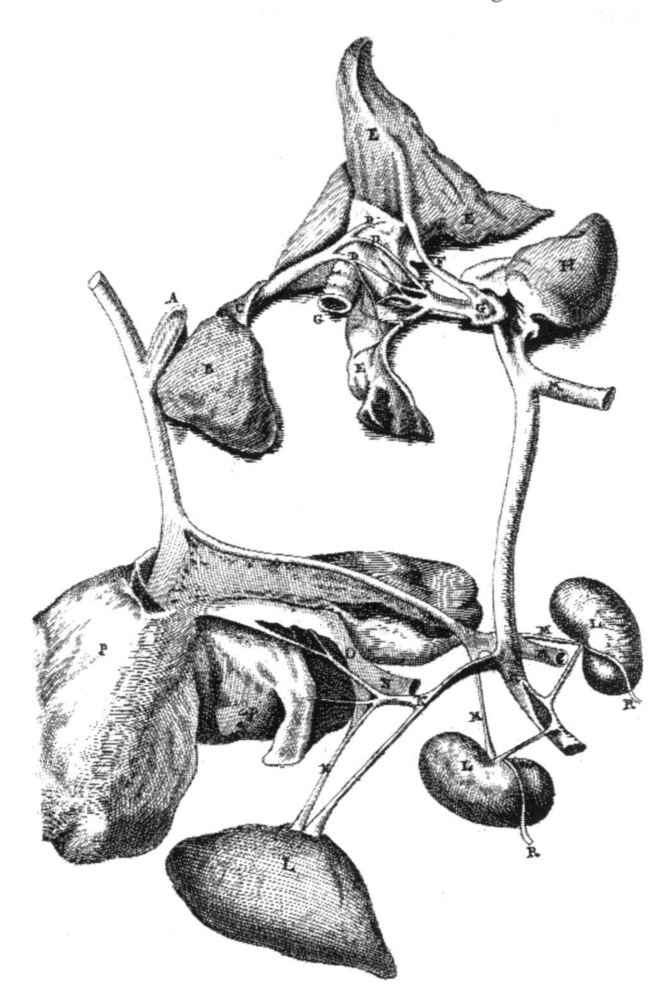

Stensen's drawing of the circulation of the blood. The heart is divided into two to show the circulation to the lungs and the rest of the organism. The most important points are: (A) the right auricle, (B) the right ventricle, (C) the outlet to the pulmonary artery, (D) veins from the pulmonary artery shown in the lung tissue, (E) the lungs, (F) veins from the lungs to the left auricle, (G) left auricle, (H) left ventricle, (I) aorta with veins to the kidney and spleen, (L) and liver (P), (M) veins from the liver to the vida cava, (O) portal vein to the liver, (N) portal vein's opening, (R) urinary ducts.

> have not been able to prove it. Schenck has not seen anything other than a small vessel which is found in the mammary glands themselves and which goes from them to the nipple. He declares this to be the case even though he admits that pressing on the small vessels causes the milk to flow out of the nipple. I think that it is very unlikely that small vessels come from further inside for then to proceed directly to the nipple. If this was the case then the breast's glandular tissue would have no function, and, furthermore, it would not be possible to to dissect a breast full of milk without damaging these small vessels, with the result that the milk would flow. The last is contradicted by experience, and the first defies common sense.[E 11]

Stensen concludes his argument by maintaining that milk is produced by glands in the breast and that these are connected to the lymph system.

Stensen also studied the anatomy of fishes and in two letters to the Dutch physician Willem Piso, written in 1664, he describes the dissection of two skates. The letters were later published in his essay on muscles and glands. He discusses the dark spots on the skin of the creature where liquid is formed which gives it a slimy quality. He also compares the glands with corresponding organs in other fish. In his description of the digestive canal, he notes that the skate has no oesophagus and that the intestinal canal has a tiny mesentery (the fold of peritoneum attaching some part of the intestinal canal to the posterior wall of the abdomen) and so is almost free-standing within the abdominal cavity. One of the two skates was fertilized. Stensen compares the development of the foetus in the placenta with that in mammals and points out that the blood of the mother and the foetus are not mixed. On this he writes:

> The uterus is built up in such a way that it functions like that of the egg's three outer layers. This helps keep the foetus warm whilst it is being carried and, at the right time for birth, to its being brought into the light. The uterus differs from the

> expelled egg by not, from the beginning, accommodating all of it, which is necessary for the development and growth of the foetus. Whilst the foetus slowly grows, the uterus receives new food supplies from the mother. There is, nevertheless a similarity between the foetus in the egg and that in the uterus, in that neither has any connection with the mother's blood vessels, even though up to now most people here assumed the opposite.(E 15)

Stensen studied the many blood cells in the skate's gills, and of this he wrote:

> What kind of function can the many series of blood vessels have, which the gills are so well endowed with, other than that blood they hold will undergo a change via its surroundings. That can be either through the blood emptying out something from itself to its surroundings, or receiving something from its surroundings, or perhaps, that both occur in one and the same process? Whether the encompassing matter passes one way or the other is of no significance, so long as it comes into contact with the outer parts of the blood vessels. For this at least is certain about the breathing: it is necessary that there is a constant supply of fresh water or air to the outer vessels. (E 15)

Stensen hints in his writing that there is an exchange of oxygen and carbon dioxide in the lungs and the gills. The physiology of breathing was first explained when Lavoisier discovered oxygen in 1775. Harvey had a clear understanding that the large volume of blood which passes through the lungs, not only serves to nourish the lung's tissue, but, and here he supported the view of Aristotle and Galeno, the function of the lungs is to cool the blood. Anatomists in Stensen's time explained the change in the colour of the blood from dark red (oxygen starved blood) to light (oxygen rich blood) by the blood being filtered through the fine pores which they thought were found in the heart's internal walls.

The Spanish physician and theologian, Michael Servetus (1511–1553) had, some seventy-five years before

Harvey, given a very accurate description of the blood's circulation from the heart to the lungs, where the dark blood from the right ventricle is cleaned of impurities by contact with the intake of air, so getting a lighter colour before being led back to the left ventricle. He argued that the blood cannot pass through the wall of the heart. The description of the circulation through the lungs was published, in 1553, in the theological work *Christianisma restituto* – 'Christianity regenerated'. He discusses respiration in the chapter dealing with the Holy Spirit and in relation to his description of the other linguistic uses of the words 'spirit' and 'soul'. The theological content of the book had been seen as heretical, and Servetus was reported to the Inquisition by Calvin of all people, and condemned to death at the stake. He managed to escape from the prison to Geneva, but was here accused by Calvin personally of heresy and again condemned to being burned at the stake. This time he failed to escape and was burned, along with 1,000 copies of his book in 1553. The original manuscript was burned to a cinder on the same occasion. Today only two copies of the book are known to exist, and this might, to some degree, explain why Servetus was not referred to for more than 150 years after his death. The few who knew of his writing on the lungs and the physiology of the blood had to be extremely careful, for it could be dangerous to speak of or quote a man who had been condemned for heresy both by the Inquisition and by his opponents in Geneva.

One of the few who knew of Servetus' discovery was Thomas Bartholin who, in a letter, wrote of the 'secret of the blood's circulation'. It is possible that Stensen learned of this from his teacher and that can be the reason for his being so careful in his discussion of the exchange of matter in the skate's gills. He refers to no observations in support of his supposition. This is in marked contrast to his other research, where he so painstakingly, step by step, justifies the reasons for his suppositions either from his own observations or those of others. This caution can explain why he cannot name the source of his knowledge – the physician and theologian Servetus who was twice condemned to death for heresy. As late as 1723, some 200 years after Servetus' death, the Bishop of London confiscated a copy of 'Christianity regenerated' which the physician Mead had copied.

The short essay 'Dissection of a shark's head' is best known for the last section which deals with the teeth and the formation of fossils. Several anatomical discoveries are dealt with in this first section, among which are the Lorenzian ampules. These form a system of mucous filled canals opening, for the most part, around the mouth, but also spread around the shark's head. Stensen assumed that their function was to secrete mucous which is correct, but, in addition, they are a sophisticated sensory organ whose significance is still not completely clear. The shark's lateral line system was also described here for the first time. Stensen writes that he had seen the lateral line in eels and several other fish, but admits that he cannot explain the organ's function. He discusses the cartillage column in the eye socket of the fish. Previously it had been thought that this was the optic nerve. By measuring the cross section of the nerves which exit from the brain, he came to the correct conclusion that the movements of the shark are not controlled from here, but from the spinal cord.

The zoologist Professor Ragner Spärk has read 'Dissection of a shark's head' and in an article in *Stenoniana* (1933) wrote:

> Stensen's account of the anatomy of the shark's head makes surprising reading for a present day zoologist, because it is so 'modern'. This impression is, in part, due to the clarity of the account and, partly, to the fact that Stensen saw so much and correctly so. With Stensen there is little of the fanciful exaggeration one finds so often in the seventeenth century natural sciences' literature. [...] His account of the shark's head is praiseworthy because it is both good and painstaking – and because so much that is new is discussed for the first time: the lateral line, the Lorenzian ampules, the relationship of the

brain to the spinal cord and the cartillage column in the eye socket. The clear and temperate explanations, the quantitative and physiological insights go far beyond the seventeenth century, making this a classic essay, in the true meaning of the term.

Founder of new sciences

It began with a shark's head

Stensen was not the first to notice the similarity between the tongue-like stones and the shark's teeth. Michaelis Mercati, natural scientist and priest had decided, from his investigations, that a shark's teeth were one thing and the tongue-like stones another. Stensen, with his knowledge of anatomy was able to demonstrate that not only was there an external similarity but also one of structural detail. Of this he says in his treatise:

> To now end this digression, I will use some of what I've deduced about the great tongue-like stones. That they are like shark's teeth is clearly evident from their shape, as the surface, edge and base are very similar to the corresponding parts of the teeth. If we are to believe the reports, new islands continue to rise up in the middle of the sea, and who knows what was Malta's first cradle. Perhaps when it was in earlier times covered by the sea, it provided a hiding place for sharks, whose teeth were buried in the sea bottom, but that after this shifted, as a result of subterranean activity, the teeth came to be found in the middle of the island. It is not surprising that such a large number of tongue-like stones have been found in Malta, for one can count over two hundred teeth in one fish, with new ones appearing every day.

A shark has several rows of teeth in its jaw. When those in the front row gradually wear out, they are replaced by the row behind moving forward to fill the empty space. The teeth take on different shapes according to which part of the jaw they occupy, so that experts can tell by studying a single tooth where in the jaw precisely it has come from. The large tongue-like stones were from the extinct shark species, *Carcharodon megalodon*, which lived in the last part of the miocene age. The teeth that have been found can be up to sixteen cms long by twelve cms wide. Conservative estimates suggest this species was almost twice as long as today's white shark, *Carcharodon carcharias*, or between twelve and fifteen metres, with a likely weight of around fourteen tons.

By the time Stensen came to publish his essay, the shark's head was in such a poor condition that it was no longer possible to make a decent drawing of it. Instead he borrowed from a friend various engravings taken from Michaelis Mercati's *Metallotheca Vaticana*.[8] Stensen is said to have remarked that these indicated that the shark's head must have been pretty shrivelled when it was drawn, for Stensen himself was known for being painstakingly accurate in reproducing every detail in his own drawings. This is shown most clearly if one compares his rendering of the shark's brain and eye with the copy of Mercati's figure.

Ideas about the earth's past were very rudimentary in the middle of the seventeenth century. Leonardo da Vinci had claimed that the origin of the fossilized remains of animals and plants was organic, but he had not given his reasons. Most people, however, believed that fossils were the product of some mystic power in the earth – *vis plastica*. The story of creation given in the Bible was the starting point for understanding the earth's origin. Only a few examined the earth's strata, most people being satisfied with speculation and sophistry, neither of which had any basis in reality. An example of this is the work of Athanasius Kircher, *Mundus subterranus* (The world underground). Published in 1644 it extended to several

---

[8] Mercati's (1541–1593) work existed as a manuscript only. It was first published in 1717.

hundred pages. Kircher drew a comparison between the world and the human body, asserting, amongst other things, that the mountains were the earth's skeleton.

When Stensen realized that the tongue-like stones (Latin *glossopetræ)* must be fossilized sharks' teeth, the question arose as to whether or not all stones and impressions which looked like living animals incarcerated in stone, were the remains of plants and animals that had lived in earlier periods of the world's history.

The study of fossils

Tuscany's diverse geology provided Stensen with rich opportunities for further investigations. Viviani who knew Tuscany well, pointed out areas where he could expect to find the remains of dead animals. The first collection of fossils consisted mainly of mussel and snail shells. By comparing these with living creatures, Stensen recognized that the fossils were the remains of living organisms. Most of the fossils were encased in stone – but how had they got there?

Further investigation of the geological deposits revealed that they consisted of horizontal layers (strata) of varying degrees of hardness and colour, which had split in some places. It gradually became clear to Stensen that identical fossils were to be found in the same kinds of sediment, even when they were a long way from each other. The strata could appear at different angles, in some cases being in the vertical plane. For the most part the fossils were the remains of creatures similar to those that now lived in the sea, with Stensen identifying oysters, scallops and snails.

Stensen published his observations in the treatise 'Dissection of a shark's head'. There is nothing in the title to suggest that the content shifts, towards the end, from anatomy to geology. He remarks merely that in this part of the treatise he has made a digression. Stensen summarizes

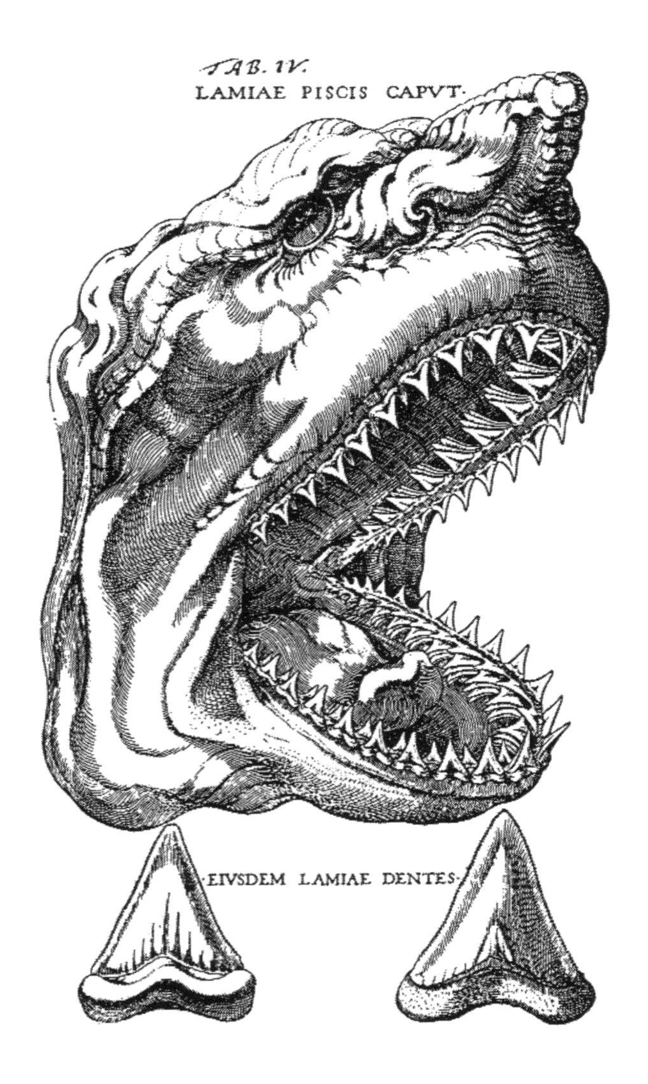

The figure that Stensen borrowed from an earlier work by Michaelis Mercati, so as to illustrate a treatise on the dissection of a shark's head, published in 1667. Stensen notes that only six rows of teeth are drawn, whereas he had counted thirteen. The tongue in the picture is something the artist must have imagined. At the bottom are two teeth, on the left, the front (nearest the lip) and on the right, the back (nearest the tongue).

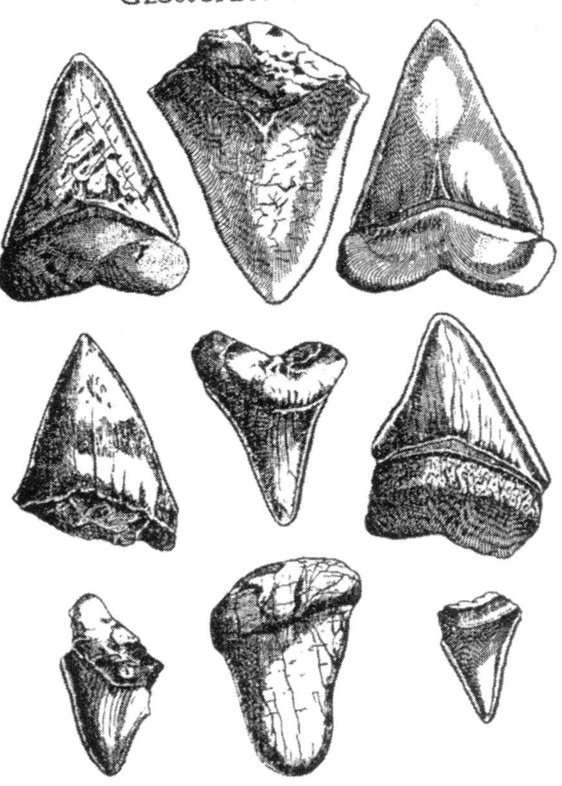

Drawings of the great tongue-like stones that Stensen showed were fossilized sharks' teeth. Stensen also took this illustration from Mercati's work.

his observations on sediments in six *conjecturæ*, in which he refers to the strata as 'this earth'. The working hypotheses in the treatise were:

Hypothesis I

The solid bodies which resemble parts of animals and which are to be found in the earth are not a product of the earth. Nor do they appear to have been formed in our times. The greatest concentrations are often in the upper, soft strata, because the soil between the bodies (fossils) has been washed away. These bodies are softer the deeper they lie and crumble easily on being touched. The reason is not, as one might suppose, that they are soft because they are still being formed. The bodies, which are soft when they are formed, contain, however, a kind of gluey substance which holds together the individual parts. The bodies we are talking about here contain more of this substance and become as powder when touched. It seems, therefore, that their softness is evidence of destruction not production.

In all probability the bodies are incapable of being formed in solid ground, when everything is of the same consistency as the mountain, and all sides are surrounded by this material. If they were to be produced today, the enveloping parts must be in a position to give way so as to accommodate the bodies that are growing. [Stensen here rejects Kircher's theory of *via plastica* – a mystical power in the earth].

Hypothesis II

It is assumed that this same earth could not have been compact when the fossils were formed. It is possible for bodies that grow slowly to lift, in the act of growing, heavy things that lie above them. It cannot, however, be gainsaid that bodies which are formed in this way must have their growth checked. This happens with the roots of trees which in hard ground are twisted and squeezed in countless ways, getting in the process quite a different shape to those that grow in softer ground. The bodies which I speak of here are all the same no matter whether they occur in soft ground in the mountain or are taken from living animals. As none of these bodies are deformed, it would seem unlikely that the ground was compact when they were formed.

Hypothesis III

It seems not unlikely that, in some earlier age, this earth has been covered by water. This can have happened in one of two ways, dependent upon whether we assume that the piece of land has always occupied the same place or has shifted its position. We learn from Holy Scripture that when the world was created it was covered with water and was so again at the time of the Flood. Some believe that this is why we can today find the mussels and snails of the sea in the mountains. In both cases the water was stagnant and carried nothing with it. One should, therefore, expect to see such bodies everywhere and not just in high places.

We see the rain's power in the level places at the foot of the mountains, which are full of pieces that have been scraped from them. It is not, therefore, so surprising, that such bodies which are laid bare on the mountain can be covered by earth in the lower areas [erosion].

There is nothing to contradict the assumption that the strata in those places where one can dig out such bodies has, at one time, shifted. If we look at the vertical cracks in the strata, these can be filled by matter of one and the same colour, in places where the strata have a different colour. It must, therefore, be thought likely that this earth has been shaken and broken by a violent movement, fallen back again, so arriving at a new position. It is easy to point out, from a number of examples, what enormous changes to the earth are often brought about by earthquakes. When even this very earth's outer form, together with examples from other places, indicate that earlier it must have had a different position and at the same time been less compact, we can, therefore, assume that the earth, before it changed position, must have been covered with water that made it soft.

Hypothesis IV

> There seems nothing against the assumption that this earth was once mixed up with water. It is well known that sand and mud are easily mixed with water that is moving rapidly and is then easily carried away with the current. Solid bodies can lie hidden in the water in two ways, either as powder, or in an elementary form. [Stensen distinguishes clearly here between suspension and decomposition.]

Hypothesis V

> I cannot see what should prevent us from assuming that this earth is a watery sediment, which has accumulated slowly. We have just seen that there is nothing wrong in assuming that this earth has been mixed with water, but it is clearly to be seen that in different places it is made up of strata of different colours, which lie on top of each other. Indeed, even if the strata are of the same colour, it is nevertheless possible to make out the individual strata from each other. So the strata themselves lead us to believe that this earth is a sediment of water. The fact that the strata are different, gives us grounds for believing that the earth has been deposited bit by bit, although we remain to be fully convinced.

Hypothesis VI

> Nothing seems to contradict the view that the bodies we can dig out of the earth and which resemble parts of animals, can be assumed to be the remains of such animals. The earth from which today one digs out bodies, which resemble parts of animals, has not itself created them. As it is likely that, in earlier times, the earth has been soft and mixed with water, how can it not be assumed that the bodies are the remains of creatures that lived in those waters?

From the six hypotheses it was possible for Stensen to explain the formation of fossils and so lay the foundation of the science of paleontology, the study of animals and plants in the geological past. He shows that changes in the

Stensen carrying out field work outside Florence. A fresco by Oscar Matthiesen (1865-1957) on the staircase of the Geology Museum in Copenhagen.

earth's crust are going on constantly and that such changes have occurred in earlier periods. This earth has, then, a history. *Geology* as a science was founded.

De Solido

For several months after the publication of the 'Dissection of a shark's head', Stensen continued his investigations into the richly variegated Tuscan geology. The area is an excellent starting point for the study of the origins of most kinds of rock with the exception of the volcanic.

His work on fossils, minerals and crystals – solid bodies that are naturally embedded in other solid bodies, was first published in Latin in 1669 in Florence, and is reckoned to be the founding work of geology and paleontology. Stensen's choice of title unites in an inimitable way the characteristics that are common to paleontology and mineralogy. The work was already translated into English by 1671 thanks to the influence of Ray and Lister at the Royal Society. A new Latin edition came out in Leiden some ten years later, in 1679. A third Latin edition was published in Florence in 1763. The work was not translated into Danish until 1902 and into Russian in 1957. Amongst geologists and Stensen scholars the work is referred to as *De Solido* or *Prodromus*. Today – 300 years after its publication – it is still reckoned to be amongst the 100 most important works in natural science.

Stensen had concluded, in his treatise on the shark's head, that the earth's bed consists of sediments formed by a fluid. He amplifies this in *De Solido*, writing of the sedimentation process:

> The finely dispersed matter of which the strata are made up can only have acquired their shape by being suspended in water, and then deposited in it by virtue of their own weight and got a smooth exterior through the movement of water on them. The larger bodies in the strata have followed the forces

NICOLAI STENONIS
DE SOLIDO
INTRA SOLIDVM NATVRALITER CONTENTO
DISSERTATIONIS PRODROMVS.
AD
SERENISSIMVM
FERDINANDVM II.
MAGNVM ETRVRIÆ DVCEM.

FLORENTIÆ

Ex Typographia ſub ſigno STELLÆ MDCLXIX.
SVPERIORVM PERMISSV.

Frontispiece of *De Solido* which was dedicated to the Grand Duke of Tuscany. The treatise consists of 76 pages and describes the founding principles of geology and crystallography.

> of gravity, both as regards the position of each individual body, and their position relative to each other. The material has laid itself so precisely around the bodies that it has filled up even the tiniest of holes – and given the surface which touches them, its smooth and shiny exterior, even if the powder, because it is uneven, does not actually lend itself to being either shiny or smooth.

Stensen reckoned that the strata containing organic remains were younger than those '... which at the time of the Creation were deposited by the original fluid'. Stensen drew a distinction between sea deposits where there were signs of sea-salt and sea creatures, and freshwater deposits that contained the remains of land plants and animals. In strata containing coal, ash, pumice, pitch or cinder he was able to demonstrate that fire (volcanic activity) had been active in the neighbourhood. Stensen assumed that new strata were always formed in the horizontal plane and that later changes in direction were the result of the influence of fire or water. These powers could undermine more solid strata, which over time could cause them to collapse and change direction. He notes that such powers were the main reason for the creation of new mountains, although these could also be formed by an 'eruption of fire hurling out ash and stone with sulphur and asphalt, or through the powerful effects of rainwater and rivers'.

Stensen formulated four basic rules for stratification (i.e. the depositing and sequencing of the strata in different periods):

1. The overlay principle: that younger strata are always deposited on top of older strata.
2. The principle that all strata are deposited in a horizontal plane.
3. The sequence of strata is constant.
4. Subsequent movements of the earth's crust can break up strata resulting in a non-horizontal relocation.

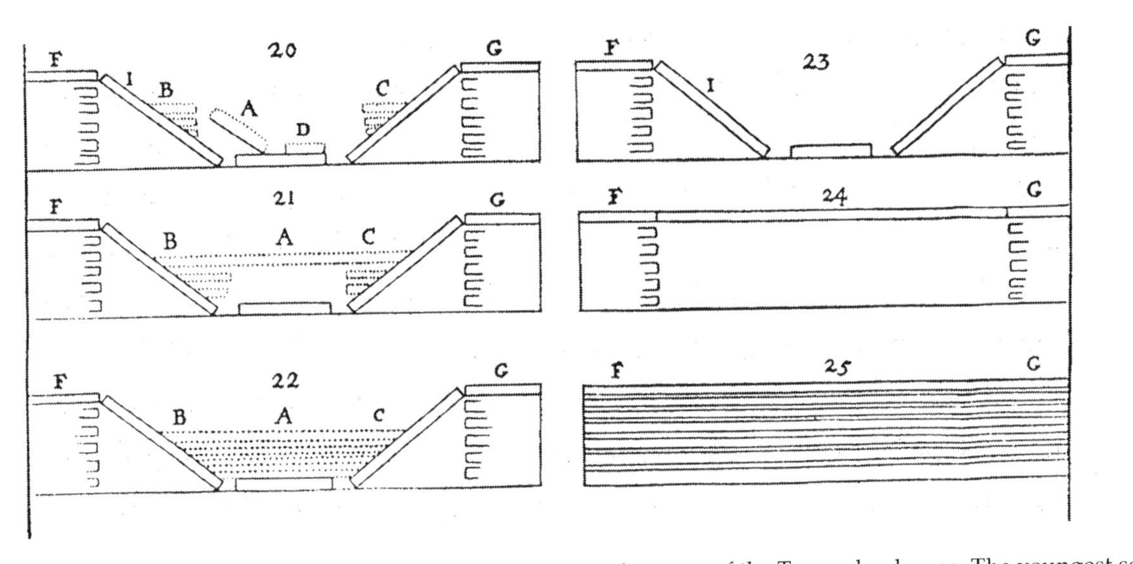

Six figures drawn by Stensen in *De Solido* (1669) to show the development of the Tuscan landscape. The youngest sediments lie at the top, so that the figure must be seen in reverse order in order to arrive at a chronological description. Drawing 25 shows a cross section of Tuscany when the strata were still intact and placed horizontally. 24 shows that some of the lower strata have disappeared as the result of the effect of water or fire, but that the upper layers are undamaged. 23 shows the formation of mountains and valleys, as a result of the upper strata breaking up. 22 shows the formation of new strata when the area is again covered by the sea. 21 shows that some of the lower strata have been eroded away without the upper layer of sandstone being affected. 20 shows that new mountains and valleys are formed when the sandstone strata breaks up.

In his account of stratification, Stensen shows that the bedrock is the lowest strata and dated 'from when the world's foundation was laid'. Stensen points out that most fossils are the remains of marine life and that the substances in which they are embedded are old marine sediments. He writes that over the course of time they either remain freestanding or are turned into sand – or limestone. Sedimentation always takes place in the horizontal plane, and he discusses the geological forces which must have acted on and resulted in the current location of the strata. He explains also how mountains are formed through the interplay of different physical forces.

Stensen produced a regional geological account of the development of the Tuscan landscape. He was able to demonstrate that Tuscany must have gone through six different geological epochs. Twice it had been covered by water, twice the landscape had been level and dry and twice uneven. Stensen provides no actual lengths for the different geological periods and, in fact, no precise dates are to be found in *De Solido*. A closer study of the many different fossils soon got several scholars to realize that the earth must be considerably older than was generally assumed at the time, namely 4000 years before the birth of Christ. To square the scientific data with the account of creation given in the Bible created insurmountable problems for geologists in subsequent years.

Stensen discusses in *De Solido* how both minerals and living organisms require liquid in order to grow:

> If a solid body is produced according to the law of nature, then it is formed by liquid. By examining the creation of solid bodies, both the origin and later growth can be studied. A body grows as a result of new particles being secreted from the fluid that surrounds it and through being deposited on top of the existing particles. The process of deposit takes place either directly from the outer fluid or through the contribution of one or more inner fluids. [Stensen is here differentiating between blood fluid and other bodily fluids.]

There is a remarkable clarity in the train of thought followed by Stensen both in his analysis and in his conclusions. Today we know that a crystal is formed as a result of new molecules in a particular pattern being deposited in a liquid on top of those that are already crystallized. The form of the individual molecule is, according to modern crystallography, the reason why a specific mineral always produces crystals of a particular form. The growth within an organism demands the supply of food-stuffs and oxygen, with the cells of a living organism growing as a result of the foodstuffs, once broken down, being built into the existing structure of the cells.

Crystals and their formation are also discussed in *De Solido*. Stensen explains the creation of quartz crystals as follows:

1. A crystal grows as the result of new crystalline material being deposited on top of the existing crystal.
2. The new crystalline material is not deposited on all the surfaces of the crystal, but most commonly on the end-points or the outer surfaces.
3. The crystalline material is not deposited on all the outer surfaces at the same time or to the same extent.
4. A surface is not always completely covered with new crystalline material; some specific parts remain uncovered, now and then the edges and now and then, the middle of the surface.

Stensen's observations are impressive. It took 300 years before research on the growth of crystals, involving the use of X-rays which can reveal the topography of crystal surfaces, confirmed them. Stensen adopted a cautious approach on the issue of what actually brought about the form of a crystal. He called it a fine *fluidum* and compared it to magnetic power. In view of the fact that, at that time, nothing was known of molecular and atomic theory, shows just how remarkable was Stensen's insight.

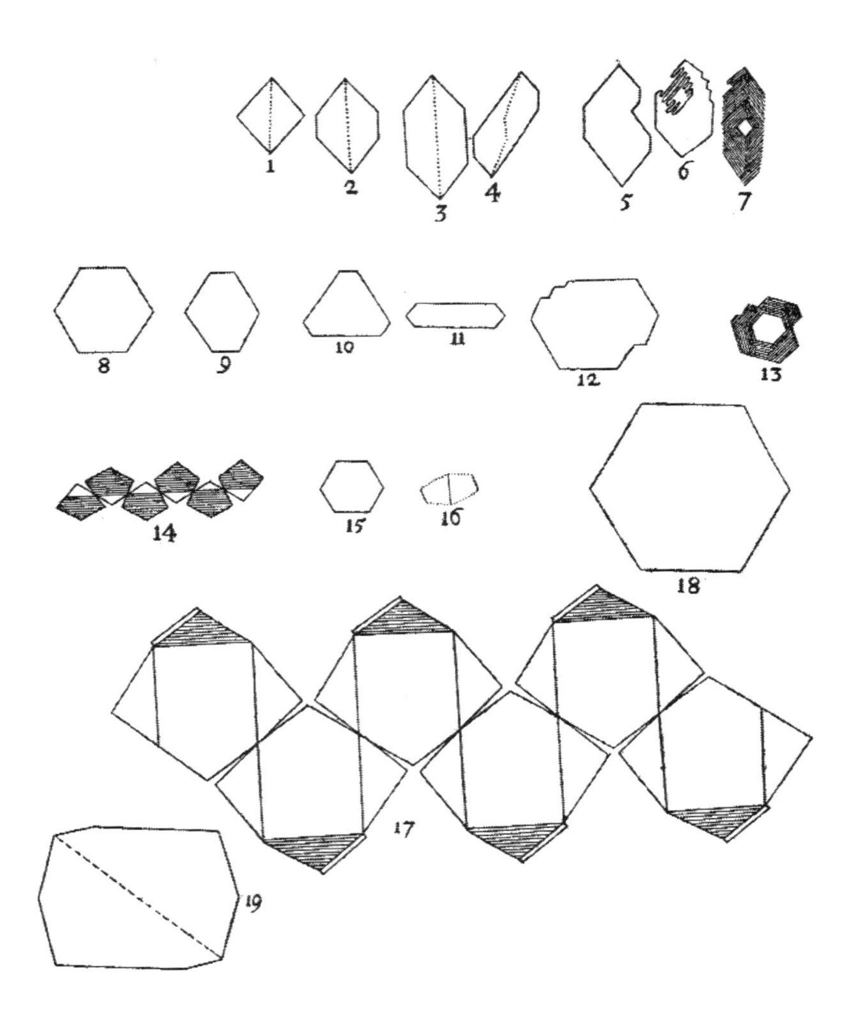

Stensen's drawings of crystals in *De Solido* (1669). The first 13 figures are of various quartz crystals drawn lengthwise and in cross section. The remaining six are of hematite. In his commentary to figures 5 and 6, Stensen writes: 'In various longtitudinal sections, the number of sides and their length will vary in different ways without the angles between the sides being changed.' This is the first time the constancy law of crystals was formulated.

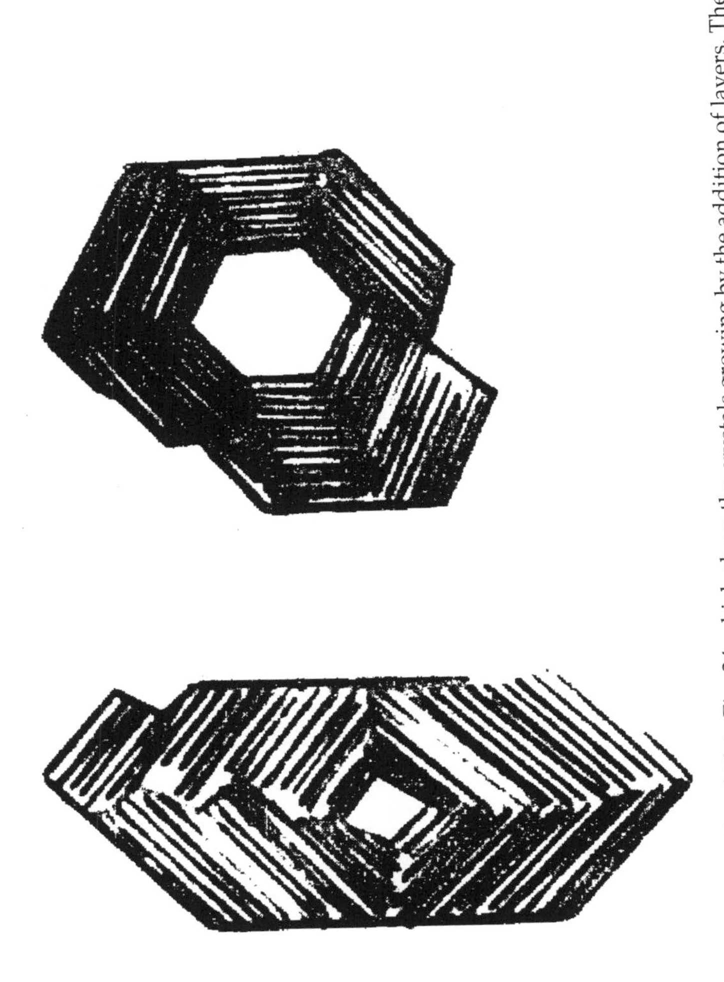

Enlargement of drawings no. 7 and 13 in Fig. 34 which show the crystals growing by the addition of layers. The growth of new material occurs in different parts of a crystal, a phenomenon that was not remarked upon again 300 years.

In addition, Stensen measured the angles of crystals with great accuracy. He did this by drawing the outline of the crystal on a piece of paper. More than 100 years was to elapse before the Frenchman Romé L'Isle discovered the goniometer which made it possible to measure the angles of crystals with greater accuracy. Stensen's drawings of crystals have been checked on two occasions by Tertsch in 1956 and by Mieleitner in 1967. They found that the greatest discrepancy from the true angle was between 2½ and 3½ degrees, which is an insignificant difference.

Stensen also noted that water and air is to be found trapped inside many quartz crystals. From the explanations accompanying the drawings and illustrations Stensen produced in his book, it appears that he had established the 'constant angle law' for crystals. The law, which has got the name *Stenos Law*, says that the angle between adjacent surfaces of a crystal of the same kind is always the same. Although it often seems that the angles characteristic of a specific crystal are 'absent', this is because such a crystal can form dissimilar surfaces. The law is, however, of general validity as it embraces all possible crystal surfaces of a specific type. The relationship between the surfaces on one and the same crystal type are therefore fixed and depend upon the arrangement of its atoms. The relationship between the size of the surfaces is determined by other factors and is of secondary importance. These are the basic rules of all modern research in mineralogy.

Stensen's research was not confined to quartz crystals. He also discusses, briefly, hematite, diamond and marcasite. Stensen was so far ahead of the scientific understanding of his contemporaries, that his theories were not accepted until much later. Possibly the theories propounded in *De Solido* would have caught on sooner had his Tuscany field notes been preserved and published. Unfortunately all of these were lost.

Subsequent fate of Stensen's geological work

In 1676, Niels Stensen received a visit from Holger Jacobæus and Caspar Bartholin, the son and nephew respectively of Thomas Bartholin. Both had been promised chairs at the University of Copenhagen once they had acquired the relevant qualifications; Bartholin in anatomy and Jacobæus in geography and history. They stayed some six months in Florence which they used to further their studies. Jacobæus was strongly influenced by Stensen and, at one point, was on the point of converting to Catholicism. Stensen was now a priest in Florence and had abandoned his plans to complete a major work in geology. He, therefore, gave to Holger Jacobæus the material he intended to use for an extended edition of *De Solido,* in the hope that the budding young professor would be able to make use of it. It was, therefore, very unfortunate that the notes were lost by Jacobæus in the course of his return journey to Copenhagen. This we learn from a letter from Jacobæus to the librarian Magliabechi in which he remarks that some of his baggage was lost during his journey home.

From notes left by Jacobæus it appears that he used much material from *De Solido* in his lectures and also drew on several of the book's illustrations, but he added nothing from his own research. It is reasonable to suppose, therefore, that Stensen's unpublished manuscript has gone missing or that Jacobæus did not understand its content.

Some have, very perceptively, spoken of the essay as the outline of a much larger work. Several contemporary researchers who read *De Solido* rightly sought for a proper documentation for the theories put forward by Stensen. Ole Worm's grandson and namesake wrote a thesis in 1686, on 'glossopetræ'. He was unable to follow Stensen's argument that the tongue-like stones were really sharks' teeth. Chemical experiments were carried out in Ole Borch's laboratory in an attempt to refute the notion that the tongue-like stones were of organic origin. Thomas Bartholin reviewed the English edition of *De Solido* in his journal *Acta medica & philosphica Hafniensia* in 1673 and revealed how little he had understood of Stensen's work when he wrote: 'The author is principally concerned with "glossopetræ" and other stones which are found in the earth or in other solid bodies.' Copenhagen, then, quickly distanced itself from Stensen's understanding of geology, because it had not understood that the organic material in sharks' teeth had been replaced by inorganic material in the tongue-like stones.

Stensen's theories on fossils also received widespread criticism. Not even Martin Lister, who was one of the first to obtain a copy of the English edition of *De Solido*, was able to accept that fossils had once been organic material.

The geologist Stensen was, therefore, soon forgotten in Denmark and Norway. When Erik Pontoppidan, who was Bishop of Bergen, published in 1752 *The first attempt at a natural history of Norway*, he remarked that he had seen many stones embedded in other stones, but he made no mention of Stensen.

Leibnitz was impressed by Stensen's scientific endeavours and wrote about them in a letter to Kr. Philip, dated 11 March 1681 (*Abhandlungen der Jablonowskischen Gesellschaft*, 1846, p. 36):

> One must admit that everything Stensen has contributed to science is of the highest quality, but that which deserves the greatest attention is his work on fossils. I have often encouraged him to continue with this scientific work and to draw the consequences of it, so as to clarify the origins of humanity, the Great Flood and other beautiful truths which could confirm what the Holy Scriptures teach us.

Leibnitz took his starting point in Stensen's geological work when he described the development of the earth's crust, and put forward the theory that the earth had originally been an incandescent mass.

In the centuries that followed the most important

contribution to geology cam from two countries, England and, above all, Italy. At the beginning of the eighteenth century, Vallisneri, basing his work on Stensen's essays, examined fossils in strata across the whole of Italy. The Italian Tozzetti, also using Stensen as his starting point, made a special study of Tuscany's geology. Both these scholars were pupils of Michelet who, in turn, had been a pupil of Francesco Redi.

The stratification principle had been used, in 1725, by the Englishman John Strachey, when he produced the world's first geological map. There is no doubt that he had read the English edition of *De Solido*. It also seems likely that the book influenced Hooke, who was, at that time making a study of earthquakes and other geological phenomena.

It was, however, not until the beginning of the nineteenth century that Stensen's geological work was really rescued from oblivion. That was done by Alexander von Humboldt who made a special point of giving Stensen great credit for his study of stratification. Slowly Stensen's geological works became better known and accepted and at the Second International Geological Congress in 1891 which was held in Bologna – it attracted more than 1000 delegates – a wreath was laid on Niels Stensen's grave in Florence and a marble memorial plaque erected. The inscription paid tribute to Niels Stensen as the founder of geology.

The word 'geology' comes not, however, from Stensen but from the Norwegian, Mikkel Pedersøn Escholt (1600–1699), who was a priest and scholar. He became the castle chaplain at Akershus in 1646 and in 1660 the vicar of Våler. In 1657 he wrote *Geologica Norvegica* which dealt with earthquakes in southern Norway, as well as containing some reflections on other geological topics. The book was published in Kristiania in 1657, the first academic work to be published in Norway. It appears likely that this was the first time the word 'geology' had appeared in print. When the book appeared in an English translation in 1662, the work entered the world's literature.

Over the years many have wondered why Stensen never completed the great work on geology that he had planned, but gave up research in this area. He had described *De Solido* as a preliminary account of his research and in Florence he had the best possible working conditions for further studies. There is no sign that his interest in geology had flagged. On his long journey through south-east Europe in 1668–69, he visited areas where he could study mining, amongst them the salt works at Hall and the emerald mines at Habachdalen.

He made one of his last geological excusions in the summer of 1671 when he travelled to Gresta in the Alps, not far from Lake Garda, and to Moncodeno, near Lake Como, in order to examine why some caves always contained ice, both in summer and winter. When he was in Copenhagen from 1672–74, as the royal anatomist, he was much engaged in studying the condition of the strata in and around the town. The situation was especially favourable for a study of the subsoil, as major excavations were taking place, the result of building activity, including new fortifications around the town. Stensen wrote to the Grand Duke about what he had seen:

> In many of the excavations around the town, two strata have been found underneath the surface of the earth, separated by a layer of clean sand. Both strata are full of pieces of tree and coal together with large quantities of different coloured amber. I have seen pieces of amber with flies and other insects trapped inside them. I have also seen a large piece in which was embedded a parcel of moving air surrounded by fluid, as one sees in crystals. One can draw many conclusions from this, including one that the entire island on which Copenhagen stands is made up of marine deposits where earlier there was no sea, but wood.[E 82]

Stensen could have continued his geological enquiries while he was a Catholic priest. History provides us with many examples of Catholic clergy who have conducted research in the natural sciences. His break with geology is all the more puzzling in that we know that while he was a bishop in Hamburg he worked on a study of the neural system. One possible explanation is that he could no longer reconcile the account of creation he found in the Bible with his own research on the history of the earth. He had seen fossils of animals and plants that were extinct and other indications that the earth was much older than was generally assumed. As a man of deep religious convictions he could not call into question the Bible's teaching, nor, as a researcher, could he conceal the observations he had made. Spinoza, published in 1670, *Tractatus theologico-politicus,* in which he demands freedom for science in relation to the Bible's teaching. We know too, that John Ray, also very devout, was unable to resolve this issue. For him the matter was expressed in doubts about his own scientific work. Peter Wagner (1986) points out that this route was not open to Stensen, for, as a believer, there had to be an agreement between his objective observations and the teachings of the faith. As a scientist, Stensen had adopted the motto: 'Precision in the experiment – agreement in the result'. If this was not fulfilled, the results were of no significance and no secure conclusions could be drawn from them. Stensen, therefore, gave up trying to find a solution to this conflict and chose instead to hand over his material to someone else and to concentrate on his vocation as a priest and pastor.

Priest and bishop

The call to the priesthood

In the summer of 1674 Stensen travelled back to Florence from Copenhagen, paying visits to Hanover and Amsterdam on the way. We do not know if he still thought of continuing his academic research when he reached Tuscany. What we do know from his letters is that he was more and more drawn to theology and felt a desire to serve God in a different way. He put his thoughts into words in a letter to the German Jesuit, Father Athanasius Kircher, on 28 May 1675:

> When I tried to repay God's goodness towards me – not that I would ever be in a position to do so – the debt seemed so huge that I was filled with a desire to give Him the best that I could, in the best way possible. When I perceived the dignity of the priesthood and that daily, at the altar, it expressed thanks for all God's goodness, forgiveness of sins and other great gifts, I begged, and was allowed, to serve God for His unblemished sacrifice for me and others. God must make me worthy of such a vocation.(E 102)

Throughout his entire life, Stensen was a believer. As a child he had been brought up in a Christian home and a workshop, with all the charitable traditions so often associated with undertakings of that nature. He had seen, during his visits to the goldsmith's workshop, how the poor and sick received help – a meal, alms and words of comfort. That religion was a cornerstone of his life is already apparent from notes made during his time as a university student. He writes in the 'Chaos' manuscript that should he ever have a family of his own, prayers and hymns would feature daily and the poor would always be welcome at his table. He vowed too that he would never speak disparagingly of his colleagues. One senses here attitudes that had been impressed upon him in his childhood home.

Stensen had an outgoing personality with winning ways, whilst his great linguistic abilities made it easier for him to establish contacts. He wrote and spoke fluent Latin, French, English, Italian and Dutch, as well as having a command of Greek and Hebrew. As a student he had been engrossed in philosophy, and in the period around his conversion, he became absorbed in heavy theological literature, both Protestant and Catholic. He gave three main reasons for his conversion to the Catholic faith: the authority of the Church's teaching, the apostolic succession and the signs of holiness.

From the day of his ordination he lived a spartan existence, using little of his income on himself, but giving most of it to the poor of his parish. In the following decade he continued this simple way of life, to the extent that he has been compared with St Francis of Assisi. His approach to his parishioners was simple and straightforward. None realized that they were in the presence of a famous scientist. His earlier success had not changed his nature, whilst his superior, Cardinal Nerli, who had feared his criticism of the priesthood, had this to say of him: 'A man of prayer, bound to God , unselfish, full of love for his fellow human beings, in particular those who are sick or in prison' (Kranz, 1978).

There is no doubt that Stensen rejoiced in his role as a Catholic priest in Florence. Earlier his intellect had been at the service of the sciences. Now he devoted his many gifts to taking care of the weakest in society. When he was summoned to be Bishop of Hanover, he hesitated for a long time. He felt he was not up to such an important position in the Church and asked instead that he might come to Hanover as chaplain. The Duke was adamant that he wanted Stensen to be the Bishop, in order that he might enjoy the greatest possible powers when engaging in the care of souls there. Stensen wrote to the Duke:

> When I compare my willingness to respond to the call with my doubts as to my ability to fulfil the office, I fear for myself – and I remind Your Highness of the example of David. Neither Samuel nor anyone else thought of him, even though he was the one that God had chosen. Perhaps God here too is hiding the one he has really chosen and that Your Highness, by thinking of others, will, in the end, find the right one. Were God not to recommend anyone else but me, and were the Pope to confirm that my calling is God's will, then I will submit to his command, and hope for all possible help from the God who alone is able to cleanse the unclean, make the unworthy, worthy and the incompetent, competent.[E 119]

The reformist Pope Innocent XI was conscientious in his choice of candidates for the office of bishop, and he, therefore, invited Stensen to Rome. After a meeting in the Vatican, the Pope recognized that Stensen was the right man for the job and a day later, on 21 August 1677, he was appointed bishop and, a short time later, Vicar Apostolic in the mission fields of north Germany and Denmark-Norway. This was the first time since the Reformation that the Kingdom of Denmark-Norway had had a member of the Catholic hierarchy responsible for spreading the faith, accredited to it. Hanover was not a bishop's see, so Stensen was appointed titular Bishop of Titiopolis in Asia Minor, the present day Turkey. His consecration took place on 19 September 1677. Stensen chose the symbol of a cross and a heart as his bishop's escutcheon. There was a double meaning here: that God's love for us is clear by Christ's death on the cross, and that faith and knowledge are as one. The heart in the escutcheon is not symmetrical, with the left side greater than the right, indicating that Stensen was aware that this was the case with the human heart.

The coat of arms of Bishop Stensen where the cross symbolizes faith and the heart the natural sciences, is shown with the left side of the heart being larger than the right. The heart is drawn as big as the cross, a sign of the unity of faith and science. Stensen adopted the symbol as a seal before he became a bishop and used it for the first time in a letter to Malpighi dated 27 October 1669.

Bishop in Hanover and Münster

Before leaving Rome, Stensen spent his time learning all he could of the situation of the Church in northern Germany and the Nordic states. The Church was weak in many parts of Germany. The frightful impact of the Thirty Years War was still apparent. In the course of the war many villages had been burnt and plundered by the hated mercenaries. More than half of the population in the country had died in the war and the material damages were greater than those of World War II. It was, above all, ordinary people who had borne the brunt of the war's destruction and who still suffered from its unhappy consequences. The result of the religious conflict left southern Germany Catholic, with the north almost wholly Protestant; the religious persuasion was no longer being determined by the political power. The clergy were not answerable to the wishes of the sovereign power. That the clergy had been in a weak position before the war had been a contributory factor in the takeover of religious affairs by the secular rulers of Germany.

Johan Fredrik's dukedom included Braunschweig-Lüneburg and was overwhelmingly Protestant. The Catholic congregation numbered around 500 and consisted mainly of foreigners employed at the palace: public servants, soldiers and artists. Two Capuchin monks also resided on the Duke's estate. Many people were employed at the huge castle where life was lived with much pomp and circumstance. Indeed the court liked to compare itself with that of the Sun King in Versailles. The Bishop's residence was more simply furnished, the household being made up of poor converts, who had been taken under Stensen's wing, rather than of courtiers. Most of those he provided for had lost their paid jobs as a result of converting to Catholicism. One of those living with Stensen but who still retained his employment was Johan von Rosen, the Captain of the Duke's Guard.

Conditions in Hanover must have been something of an

upheaval for Stensen. The warmth and Catholicism of Florence was replaced by the chill of northern Germany, religious toleration, by all the problems of the diaspora – a lack of priests, a lukewarm faith, a denunciation of others' beliefs and, not least, a lack of financial support for pastoral tasks. Of his impressions of Hanover he wrote that ' the winter was cold, but not as cold as the souls'. Bishop Stensen kept in close contact with Florence and its Grand Duke Cosimo III. They exchanged more than fifty letters during the two and a half years Stensen spent in Hanover, many of them containing requests for money to support the poor who sought his help.

The new bishop was respected for his strict and austere lifestyle. We know from contemporary accounts that he often invited many of the poor to dine with him. The parish register of Hanover reveals that during Stensen's time there, some 400 were converted to Catholicism, either by him or the Capuchin friars.

Many Protestant and Catholic clergy still entertained the hope that the churches could be re-united. At the request of Protestant colleagues, Stensen took part in negotiations for a union at Celle in 1679. The negotiations proved unsuccessful and after them Stensen remarked:

> From long experience, both as regards my own personal conversion and resulting from these talks, I have come to the conclusion that to discuss religious belief is a waste of time. Non-Catholics do not understand Catholic concepts, and Catholics, for their part, cannot say that they understand the true significance of non-Catholic concepts. (Krantz, 1978).

Stensen arrived in Münster in 1680, a year after Johan Fredrik's death. The Duke had no male heir so that the dukedom passed to his youngest brother, Ernst August, who was a Protestant. On moving into the palace he allowed Stensen to conduct Catholic services in his own house, but he ceased to provide him with a salary.

The Pope decided that Niels Stensen should be appointed auxiliary bishop in Münster. The town lay in the Catholic part of Germany with its large churches and religious houses bearing witness to an established church. However the diocesan clergy largely failed in their task of the care of souls. A century long tradition in Münster had meant that its secular ruler should also bear the rank of bishop in one or several dioceses. The result was an unfortunate amalgam of the clerical and secular powers. The Council of Trent, which ran from 1545–63, is reckoned to have been the most important in the history of the Catholic Church. It corrected many of the errors that had taken hold in the Church. The sale of indulgences and clerical offices was forbidden and the faith was given a new and clearer formulation, in order to lessen doubts on fundamental issues, amongst the believers. New directives as to the conduct of the clergy were formulated, and the bishops were enjoined to set up seminaries in their dioceses in order to ensure the spiritual and intellectual training of the priesthood. It was also decided that the bishop should reside in his diocese.

So far as Münster was concerned, several of these reforms were never carried out. The Cathedral chapter – it formed the bishop's council – consisted of forty aristocratic canons, all of whom had considerable economic and political influence. It was not unusual for disagreements between the clergy to be resolved by armed conflict. The former Prince-bishop of Münster, Christopher Bernhard von Galen (1606–1678), had, shortly before his death, been in conflict with von Mallinkrodt, one of the canons, which resulted in his besieging and bombarding the town when its population rose against him. Galen was characterized as a clerical ruler, of a baroque nature, and was the first to create a standing army in Europe. It numbered 21,000 men and was used by the Prince-bishop to prosecute several wars aimed at extending his territory.

The current Prince-bishop, Ferdinand von Fürstenberg had for a period of years been responsible for the Diocese of Paderborn, prior to his taking on Münster in 1678. The auxiliary bishop was responsible for the ordination of priests, visitations and the consecration of new churches. He did not have any administrative tasks or duties involving personnel. Stensen was still the Vicar Apostolic for Hanover, Hamburg and Denmark-Norway, when he came to Münster. He requested that he be freed of these responsibilities, but the Pope continued to want him to be in charge there. One can but assume that Rome was pleased with the results of his work. Stensen set out to carry through the reforms of the Council of Trent during his time in Münster, but the corruption was so widespread and the opposition so strong that he barely began the necessary process. Those who came after him were to carry the task forward.

In Hanover he had had a permanent household of ten, but this was reduced to three – a man servant, an alms giver and a housekeeper. Stensen got on well with his bishop, the fifty-four-year-old Ferdinand von Fürstenberg, who had many good qualities, and lived a pious life. Whilst in Münster, Stensen set himself three main tasks: priestly ordinations, visitations and spiritual guidance – primarily of priests. Most of his time was spent in travelling around the two great dioceses, which were made up of 250 parishes. In the course of three years, Stensen managed to visit around 200 of them. He visited the Diocese of Paderborn and travelled throughout Münster, Emsland and South Oldenburg where he conducted the confirmation service, consecrated churches, ordained priests, and preached several times a day. His chaplain – Schmael – said of Stensen: 'His words were persuasive, not only through the strength of his reasoning, but also through their goodness, kindliness and humility, and because of the great dignity and modesty that characterised his appearance.' (Kranz, 1978).

When visiting a parish, Stensen often chose to travel on foot in order to show his solidarity with the poor who could never afford to go by carriage. One of the bishop's most important primary duties was to ordain priests. He was also responsible for ensuring that candidates for the priesthood were suited to the calling. Stensen took his duties as seriously as he had previously taken his science. The ordinations were a source of much inner torment for he had little or no influence over the choice of candidates. It is said that for several days before he carried out the ordination of priests, he undertook a regime of strict fasting and spent much of the night in prayer, because he was afraid that he would ordain those who were not fit to serve God. At the time it was common practice for the bishop to accept payment after an ordination. Stensen would not go along with this and was therefore pretty unpopular with the other clergy – he had done away with a good source of income for them!

Stensen's income in Münster was much lower than it had been in Hanover. The Diocese was poor and savings had to be made on everything, including the salary of an auxiliary bishop. From his correspondence one can see that he had to solicit money from wherever possible: from Cosimo, the Propaganda Fund and the Curia in Rome. So as to increase Stensen's own income, his Prince-bishop appointed him parish priest at the St Ludgeri Church. Although this brought him a considerable income his outgoings were even heavier. For many of his 2,000 parishioners were very poor. The winter of 1680 was especially severe, and many came to him in extreme need. In a letter to his bishop's secretary, Ortensio Mauri, he noted that 'the poor are always with you' and continued:

> This morning, on leaving the church, I was accosted by two men and three women, yesterday I learned of a case where three small children, who had been abandoned by their parents, had died in the deepest distress. Oh that I could help all, but those whom I cannot assist by my own hand, I must assist through my prayers to God. It cuts me to the heart when I must turn away the poor – merchants of paradise – without buying their wares and that I must let the poor of Jesus leave yet again without solace.(E 210)

Stensen tried to set up an arrangement by which each of

the better-off members of the parish should look after a poor one. He didn't, in his sermons, censure the rich for their riches, but urged them to use their money wisely and to give some of it to the poor. On his becoming a parish priest Stensen's household grew once again, for he was unable to deny the poor who sought shelter. In addition he had converts living with him. Stensen was forced to borrow money in order to support so many lodgers. Grand Duke Cosimo sought to bring some sort of order to the situation. He paid the auxiliary bishop's debts and accommodated several of the converts by giving them positions in Tuscany. Stensen promised to reduce the size of his household and to live according to his means. The financial problems arising from the upkeep of the converts was eased, but he still had to look after many of the poor. To obtain money for provisions he sold most of the furniture he owned. He sold his bishop's crozier, made of silver, his ring and other liturgical objects which were made of precious metal, to obtain money for those in need. He no longer wore the ring as a sign of his status and used a wooden crozier. His work for the congregation of St Ludgeri has become legendary. The parish has not forgotten this, whilst the church in Münster too remembers him still.

During his many visitations around his dioceses, Stensen saw how parlous a situation many of the clergy found themselves in. His attempt to improve the situation took a very 'modern' form. He had the idea of writing a guide for the priests, a task he began shortly after arriving in Münster. The book *Parochorum hoc age* ('Duties of the shepherd') was completed in 1682 and published in Florence in 1684. The intention was to print 400 copies, but when the Archbishop of Florence read the manuscript, he increased the number to 1,000, so that the priests of Florence should also get a copy. 'Duties of the shepherd' was a practical guide for priests on pastoral care. Stensen wrote that a priest's first duty was to set a good example by his own conduct, and that he must have the ability to understand the 'heart's secret', which can be hidden from some people, so that, through it, they can make clear what they lack for a completely Christian life. He compares, in different sections, a priest's work with that of an army general, a gardener and a doctor. Stensen stressed the individual nature of the care of souls, giving examples such as that of the doctor who must treat each patient differently – depending on the nature of the disease and the individual it had attacked. In the same way the priest must evaluate each individual and pay a special attention to his or her 'spiritual state'.

Stensen also laid on courses for his priests, and on several occasions invited them to his home in order to give them advice and guidance on matters pertaining to the priesthood. In this way he built up a collegial sense of solidarity which helped overcome the often lax morals of the clergy. That not all was well on the moral front is evident from an undated letter – it was probably written in 1682 – sent by Stensen to one of his priests:

> I deplore most of all that the holiest of feast days are profaned in the most shameful manner. We start the day with God, but end it with the Devil, transforming the morning's benediction into the evening's evil. It is easy to see that the Devil is given more than God at holy ceremonies of baptism, marriage, the ordination of priests and the taking of vows by those in religious orders, when almost always they end with a party – and the party ends in drunkenness. What is the benefit of receiving anew the mercy of God in the morning when we trample it under foot in the evening?[E 288a]

He writes later in the letter that the next time a saint's day is celebrated, the rule of the early Christians will be observed, 'inasmuch as they comforted the poor and the sick and invited the poor to dine'.

Gradually Stensen appeared more and more wretched. At a time when a bishop, on an official visit to a parish, arrived in a carriage surrounded by pomp and circumstance, Stensen appeared plainly dressed with none of the

PAROCHORVM
HOC AGE

Seu euidens demonſtratio
quod Parochus teneatur
omnes alias occupationes
dimittere
& ſuæ attendere perfectioni
vt cōmiſſas ſibi Oues
ad ſtatum ſalutis æternæ
ipſis à Chriſto præparatum
perducat.

FLORENTIÆ MDCLXXXIV.

Apud Hippolytum Nauceſium
Superiorum permiſſu.

The first page of *Parochorum hoc age* – 'Duties of the shepherd', published in Florence in 1684. Stensen wrote the book while he was auxiliary bishop in Münster and Paderborn, as a practical guide in pastoral work for the priests in the dioceses.

outward signs of his office. The Cathedral chapter was annoyed that a superior did not dress according to his position and that his entire life style was devoid of any form of luxury. They did not like the fact that their bishop could be mistaken for an ordinary tramp as he walked barefoot along the highway!

During the time Stensen was in Copenhagen as the royal anatomist, he had the German Jesuit Johannes Sterck as his spiritual advisor. He continued to perform this function after Stensen had become a bishop. In a letter that was undated but seems likely to have come from Hanover in 1682, Father Sterck exhorts Stensen to persevere even if the fruits of his work are few and small. He also urges him to tone down his ascetism and warns him that it may be unwise to be too strict with his subordinates. Towards the end of the letter, Sterck comes to the question of Stensen's lifestyle and especially his attire. The father does not forget that he is writing to a bishop so that Stensen is addressed as 'Your Grace'.

> His Excellency [Bishop Ferdinand] has spoken to me about Your Grace and he seems to wish that you, as he put it, will pay attention to the externalities and will guard the dignity of the bishop, and I take this to refer to clothes, chaplains and servants. Allow me humbly to put forward my understanding of the matter, that you, with regard to your attire, appear somewhat below the dignity and decorum of a bishop. Nor should a auxiliary bishop forget his position by an unbecoming humility and weakness as regards seemly attire.[E 253]

The conflict between Stensen and the Cathedral chapter came to a head when a new bishop was to be elected, on the death of Ferdinand in 1683. The choice of bishop had been decided, though bribery, threats and intrigue, long before the formal election by the Cathedral chapter took place. The day before the election, Stensen was invited to say Mass, the intention being that the Holy Spirit would help the Cathedral chapter to choose the best candidate for the post of bishop. Stensen refused not only to celebrate Mass, but also to have anything to do with such a hypocritical election. Outraged he travelled to Hamburg, where he took shelter with Theodor Kerckring, the friend of his youth. In writing to Pope Innocent XI to complain of the bishop's election in Münster, he asked to be given new duties. To return to Münster was out of the question! He wrote that it was difficult to exclude unsuitable candidates for the priesthood, when the religious and worldly power was united in the person of the ruler, and where rich families with influence and power sought to get their sons ordained. He wrote finally that he had laid the matter before the Pope because he wanted to restore the glory of the Catholic name amongst non-Catholics.

A. D. Jørgenson writes in his biography of Stensen:

> He set to work with a will, sought to build up that which was neglected and engender a new spirit in the whole of church society. Of course he came into conflict everywhere with old habits and ingrained abuses, but on the other hand, he won support from all those who had cherished a religious disposition and a serious intent to live a Christian life.

Stensen is considered to be one of the leading exponents of the Counter-Reformation in Northern Europe during the seventeenth century.

Hamburg and Schwerin

Stensen soon discovered that the situation in Hamburg was not much better than in Münster. The town's congregation consisted of 600 Catholics who were served by five Jesuit priests, the two eldest of which brought the clergy into serious disrepute through their life style. Stensen was both sad and embarrassed at their bad example and wanted the two to be replaced with younger priests. He wrote privately, therefore, to their superior in Cologne, requesting that they be moved. Through a mishap the contents of the letter became public so that it soon got about that the Bishop wanted the priests replaced, something which led to Stensen personally becoming a hated figure. On several occasions his life and health were threatened by the more extreme members of the Catholic community.

Over time life had become wearisome for the Bishop of Titiopolis. He was in conflict with the Cathedral chapter in Münster and with parts of the Catholic community in Hamburg. He now felt more lonely than every before and had little opportunity to undertake the pastoral work he felt to be his vocation. This dispute with the Jesuits put a brake on his activities, and he felt himself to be both useless and superfluous in Hamburg. In a letter dated 8 November 1684 addressed to the Grand Duke he wrote:

> ... I'm of almost no use. I neither can nor will undertake anything because a large part of the congregation are furious with me. I have, therefore, chosen to preserve a complete silence so as in no way to increase the unrest.[(E 381)]

Whilst he waited for a reply from the Pope, Stensen tried to help the many poor in Hamburg to the best of his ability – as here too the need was indescribably huge. Despite requests to the contrary, he spared no pains, and continued his ascetic life style, with fasts and prayers. A reaction could not be avoided and his health began to fail. Stensen now realized that he would have to cut back on the many tasks he had taken upon himself.

Finally Niels Stensen received a reply from the Pope. He was to be Vicar Apostlic in Halberstadt, Bremen, Magdeburg, Schwerin and in areas ruled by the Dukes of Mecklenburg. This was in addition to the responsibility he already had for Hanover, Hamburg and Denmark-Norway. Stensen decided to carry out his duties in a somewhat unusual way. He would travel round the areas for which he was responsible in order to find out how conditions for Catholics could best be ordered. He outlined his plan in his reply to the Pope.

For most of the year 1684, Stensen travelled through Hanover, Bremen and Schwerin, with Hamburg as his starting point. He also planned to visit Copenhagen but found he did not have the time. He travelled in civilian dress as the law in Protestant countries did not allow the Catholic clergy to carry out their clerical duties. After his round trip Stensen was quite clear in his own mind that there was no great need for a senior figure, such as himself, in places where the different Catholic orders had the opportunity to establish themselves, but the presumption was that they lived according to the rules of their order. Stensen felt that to some degree at least his tasks in Hamburg were done. There was no need for him to be Vicar Apostolic when his investigations had shown that the post was unnecessary. His thoughts for his future surfaced in a letter to Cosimo written on 14 November 1684:

> I don't know what I shall choose to do or what advice I will give to the Congregation with regard to these vicariates. But why do I have such thoughts about the future, when I do not know whether I shall live to the morrow. He who has conducted me along roads I know nothing of, leads me now, seeing or unseeing, on his path of mercy.[E 382]

When Stensen wrote that letter he had but thirteen months to live. He was to experience yet again that God was to lead him on unknown paths. He had now been given the Pope's permission to travel to Florence and for a time withdrew from active duties in order to improve his health. Before he travelled south, he visited Copenhagen in order to say goodbye to his family and friends. He was never to see his beloved Florence and Tuscany again. Instead his travel plans were changed, and he was to spend the last year of his life working as a priest in Schwerin.

One can justifiably ask if the offer from Duke Christian Ludvig, which went only part of the way to fulfilling

Stensen's earlier wish to buy a house in which Catholic services could be held, was the only reason for his abandoning his journey to Italy. In his travels round the vicariates Stensen had seen the results of the Thirty Years War, and that especially in Schwerin, Protestants and Catholics were ranged against each other. He had always wanted to bring about a reconciliation between the confessions, a wish that had been strengthened after his visitation in Schwerin. In Hamburg he had always wanted to follow his vocation, now he had been offered the chance to do so and Stensen accepted it.

His conditions of work in Schwerin were worse than he had ever encountered. In Hamburg and Münster he had had superiors to whom he could turn, but in Schwerin he was quite alone. Nor could he operate as a bishop. The letter from the Duke made it clear that, on both politico-religious and financial grounds, he could only give Stensen the power to act as an ordinary parish priest in Schwerin. He must not give any outward sign of his being a bishop, nor exercise any of his bishop's office. Contact with Duke Christian Louis had to be by post as he lived for the most part in France. During this time in Schwerin, Stensen was visited by his friend, the convert Johannes Rosen. They had agreed to meet in Paris and travel together to Florence but now he came instead to Stensen. In Rosen we have a valuable eyewitness to Stensen's last year in Mecklenburg. Schwerin was a small town but the beautiful palace, which lay on an island in Lake Schwerin, recalled the town's years of greatness in the Middle Ages. The Gothic cathedral was now a Lutheran parish church. The Catholic congregation numbered no more than eighty and was, like almost all the diaspora congregations, on the verge of extinction. Relations between the Catholics and Protestants were very strained. As a Catholic, the Duke had many problems with his Protestant subjects and so as not to provoke them he had told his public officials to keep an eye on Stensen. His will contained a codicil to the effect that all Catholic services should cease six weeks after his death. Opportunities for conducting Catholic missionary work in the place were virtually nil.

The Duke's chaplain-in-ordinary, Father Jakob Steffani, lived in the palace and had been with the Duke for eighteen years. Stensen now worked as an ordinary priest with the congregation and lived in a private house in the town. He had been given a dispensation by the Vatican which allowed him to conduct divine service without revealing, through his attire, that he was a bishop. This was to avoid giving offence to the population. From a letter of 10 October 1686 to Nikolaus von Bunsow – one of Christian Louis' Privy Counsellors – we can perceive the kind of working conditions Stensen laboured under:

> I've been careful, and still am careful to avoid anything that could associate any kind of authority with me personally. Even when I planned to travel personally to Stockholm, I arranged instead that the credentials of the mission be given to my chaplain by another. I've been here almost a year, and Father Steffani cannot accuse me of carrying out the slightest activity in the capacity of one in authority. Even though I have baptised several children, I have left it to him to enter the names in the parish register, which I had never seen, so that one could not interpret this as an attempt at a visitation. In other words, I have promised to live as an ordinary priest, which I have done and will continue so to do.[(E 473)]

Stensen signs off the letter not as a bishop, but as 'Your most unworthy servant'. He is a bishop, but works as a priest, something others would perhaps regard as a humiliating state of affairs. Stensen, however was happy to be able to function once again as a priest and to use his time and energy to work in a parish. Nevertheless he was unable to free himself from the duties that fell to him has a bishop. As such he was forced to undertake the long journey to Hamburg on Maundy Thursday 1686 in order to officiate at the Chrism Mass. The effort was so great that Stensen asked the Holy See for a dispensation, so that for the following Easter he could hold the service[10] in Schwerin.

Father Steffani became ill and Stensen was obliged to take over more and more of the pastoral obligations of the parish. He managed to accomplish many things for the tiny congregation in Schwerin, appointing a teacher for the children and obtaining Prayer Books, for which the Grand Duke Cosimo paid. His advice on how the divided Christians could be reconciled was clear: investigate in depth any questions that emerged, be careful when commenting on the view of others, pray and above all be in oneself an example of a genuine Christian life.

When Father Steffani died, Stensen realized that if he left the place, the congregation would be unlikely to get another priest and would disintegrate. Stensen, therefore, chose to stay in Schwerin. There is however, no doubt that he longed to return to Florence and his friends there. We can gather how lonely he must have felt, when we read a letter to Cosimo, dated 23 February 1686:

> Nevertheless I dare not carry out anything in my capacity as Vicar Apostolic, but do just the work of any ordinary missionary. I live in an extremely dangerous situation, as I have no one here to advise me.[(E 450)]

Stensen felt lonely and missed a spiritual advisor; no one was available to him before he died. For most of the time he worked as a priest and a bishop in northern Germany, he was alone and received only scant support from his superiors. Nevertheless he never gave up on the demands of his priestly calling. He gave everything he had, both materially and spiritually, to the flock he had been sent to

---

[10] In the Catholic Church the holy oil which is to be used the following year is consecrated as a special Mass – the Chrism Mass. This Mass should take place in the cathedral on Maundy Thursday or some days earlier. According to an old tradition the bishop should celebrate the Mass together with as many as possible of his priests, as the Mass is also a sign of the bishop's communion with his priests.

protect. He never lost his courage and his optimism and joy affected all around him. His example was like a guiding star for his successors in the diaspora. Stensen was not to see the fruit of his work. The tiny congregation in Schwerin survived, and today there are more than 130,000 Catholics in sixty-five parishes with almost 100 priests, in what was previously the dukedom.

Niels Stensen's philosophical views and his scientific method

Stensen and seventeenth-century science

Stensen's scientific work was carried out at a time when science itself was entering a new era. The new science had brought about an almost boundless belief in reason and that with its help one could work one's way towards a holistic view of existence. Today one generally describes the revolution of the seventeenth century as the transition from antiquity's theological world view to the mechanistic, in which physical reality is described in mathematical terms. It was the task of science to reveal uniformities and prepare the ground for technological development. Knowledge should no longer be drawn from human authorities, but from experience. One's own observations and experiments were decisive, and not what the learned had written in the distant past. In order to ensure that investigations and the conclusions drawn from them were accurate, mathematics was used and became the most important tool for describing natural phenomena. Galilei had, by means of his telescope, made discoveries in our solar system which were to change our view of the world. His motto had been: *measure everything that is measurable and make measurable that which still is not!* In Florence, Stensen met Galilei's pupils and as a student, he read the astronomical works of Copernicus, Johannes Kepler and

Tycho Brahe. After Stensen's death, the founding principles of mathematical science were developed further by Isaac Newton. At about the same time, Carl von Linnaeus in Sweden was engaged in observing and classifying the objects of nature – plants, animals and minerals, and by so doing laid the formulation of biological science.

Johannes Kepler had formulated the proposition that science must seek out causes that can be physically demonstrated and not just hypothesized. Causes of this kind he called true causes – *veræ causæ*. Causes that cannot be demonstrated he reckoned to be non-existent. This way of thinking has dominated physics and the other exact sciences from the middle of the seventeenth century down to our own times.

The application of the *veræ causæ* principle is, however, only valid in a closed system which is not exposed to external influences. In the real world one is constantly faced with non-controllable factors that will influence the effect of a specific cause. By setting up experimental conditions one can reduce the unwanted external influences and so come closer to the ideal situation. Galileo Galilei tried to describe what happens when two balls collide with each other. He discovered that when he made the two balls and the surface on which they moved, smoother, it was easier to describe the path of the two balls before and after they struck. Modern physicists have reduced the friction still further, but there will always be some remaining, which influences the experimental conditions.

Stensen's scientific work was in biology and geology, two disciplines which have in common the fact that they deal with very complex natural systems. Harvey, who discovered the circulation of the blood, showed that its movement was brought about by mechanical causes, whilst Malpighi demonstrated the capillary system, with the help of his microscope. Both of these important discoveries, however, contributed nothing to our understanding of what caused the blood to flow along the vessels and what role this performed. Stensen furnished the proof that the heart is a pump made of muscle and that it causes the blood to move. By dissecting live animals and then blocking a part of the bloodstream in a branch of the aorta, he demonstrated that the body's muscles require a blood flow. The mindset of the day was dominated by the wish to describe cause and effect – and to find the laws linking them.

Stensen described phenomena from a more holistic viewpoint. He didn't try to give a detailed description of individual causes or put forward hypotheses that could not be upheld, either by experiment or observation – the formation of a fossil for example. In practice it would not be possible to describe every stage of what had gone before. Stensen could hold opinions as to how a fossil had been formed, or how it had *not* been formed, but in practical terms he could not say exactly how it had occurred. Jens Morten Hansen (2000) has pointed out that Stensen drew on the inductive method as a criterion for understanding. Aristotle was the first to describe the inductive method, which together with the deductive and the intuitive method were, according to him, the three main methods one could utilize in reasoning and the drawing of conclusions in the natural sciences. It is not, however, possible to say that Stensen must be characterized by this as a radical empiricist. Stensen belongs to the rationalism of the seventeenth century, as his relationship with Descartes clearly indicates.

Stensen and Descartes

During the siege of Copenhagen Stensen attended the lectures on mathematics given at the University by Rasmus Bartholin. Bartholin was keen on Descartes and very ready to talk to his students about his philosophy. He had studied in Leiden during his youth and had known the philosopher personally. On his return to Copenhagen, Bartholin strove to make Descartes' analytical geometry generally known in the kingdom of Denmark-Norway. Stensen must have shared his professor's enthusiasm for Descartes' teaching, for in the 'Chaos' manuscript we find many notes and references to the philosopher's works.

René Descartes was a French philosopher and mathematician. Born in 1596 he is considered to be one of the seventeenth century's great philosophers. He was the first major representative of the new era's philosophy that marked a break with the Christian thinkers of the Middle Ages, and his influence on the development of philosophy can hardly be exaggerated.

The clarity and certainty of mathematical thought is an important foundation element in Descartes' philosophy. In his work *Discourse de la méthode* – 'On method' – he formulated the following four ground rules for thought: (1) only judge something to be true if it can be perceived as absolutely clear and distinct, and is self-evident; (2) divide up each problem into simpler problems if that is possible; (3) move systematically from the simple truth to the more complex one; (4) on any occasion make sure that no factors are omitted.

In practice, Descartes' method involves the analysis of a relationship down to its smallest elements and then its reconstruction in a manner that is easy to grasp. One cannot accept something as true without first examining, step by step, with the help of reason, what is certain and evident. This was his method of attaining true understanding and it was also that which came to characterize the work of Niels Stensen. In fact he came to pursue it to an even greater extent than Descartes himself. In the 'Chaos' manuscript, Stensen writes:

> One sins against the majesty of God by not observing nature's own works, but is satisfied by reading the works of others. By doing the latter one forms and shapes different fictitious notions and misses out, not only on the enjoyment of God's miracles, but wastes time which could be used for necessary things and for the benefit of the neighbour. One fixes on things that are unworthy of God. Such are these scholastics,

> such are most philosophers who spend the whole of their lives in the study of logic. Time should not be used to explain and defend these opinions – scarcely on their examination. Hereafter I shall not use my time with these speculations, but spend it on investigation, experience and notes about objects in nature and the observance and checking of these accounts where that it possible.[N 59]

After arriving in the Netherlands to continue his education, his admiration for parts of Descartes' philosophy was to receive a setback, as his anatomical knowledge increased.

Both Descartes and Stensen belong to the seventeenth century which has been called the century of doubt and faith. It was a period characterized by a strong desire to create a world view of unity and order. At the same time the new mechanistic view of the world raised the issue as to how it could be reconciled with the spiritual principle. The relationship between dead matter and a divine creator, between body and soul and humanity's free will within the whole of the great system was the great challenge of the period – and is so still.

According to the philosophy of Descartes, the world is made up of two substances, the spiritual and the extended things. God and the consciousness of man are the thinking substance, *res cognitans*. All other bodies belong to the category extended things *res extensae*. The spiritual substance has nothing to do with size or space, it occupies nothing and takes up no room. Descartes seeks to explain mechanistically not only the phenomena of dead nature, but also living processes too. According to this view, all organisms are ingenious machines which, in principle, can be explained in the same way as inorganic matter. By analogy the human is viewed as a machine with a soul, different from animals, which are simply machines without souls. The behaviour of animals and their expressions of pleasure and pain are described as mechanistic reflexes without feelings. Stensen writes about this in a letter to Thomas Bartholin, dated 12 September 1661:

> I will at the first opportunity take up again this heavy work, even though I admit that it is not without some sense of horror that I expose living animals to such prolonged pain. The Cartesians often brag about the certainty of their philosophy. I would wish that they could make me as certain as they themselves are, that an animal has no soul, and that there is no difference between the touching, tearing apart and burning of the nerves of a living animal and the cutting up of the drive belt of a machine.[E 3]

When Stensen later investigated the glands in the eye and the lachrymal duct, he commented on Descartes' description of them in a letter to Bartholin and expresses regret that the philosopher had made a mistake when he asserted that the lachrymal fluid is secreted through the corneæ:

> What shall one say when even the shrewd Descartes in his treatise *De homine* is of the opinion that tears are secreted through these corneæ. He believes then that tears can pass from inside through the cornea, just as the ancients believed that they could be passed from the outside by evil spirits.[E 7]

By studying the finer structure of the heart's tissue, Stensen argued that it was the same as that found in the other muscles of an organism e.g. in a thigh muscle. The fact that the heart was a muscle and nothing more, overturned all the customary views one had had till then about the organ. The Greco-Roman doctor Claudius Galenos (AD 129–200) had written that the heart housed the soul and produced plasma as well as having other exalted qualities, a view shared by Stensen's contemporaries. Galenos' medical works were of great importance down to the seventeenth century. Stensen wrote about his discovery to Thomas Bartholin and the latter in his reply to Stensen dated 4 August 1663, commented:

> Certainly your observations of the muscles and the heart are excellent and worthy of publication. The spirit of Hippocrates will applaud you, because you, through your outstanding

> observations, revive his view of the heart which we have moved away from, and provide clear evidence of the fact that the heart really is a muscle. Galenos and his successors will thank you because you have established that the fibres of the heart are of one and the same kind.(E 14)

The teachings of Stensen and Descartes had overtaken Galenos' understanding of the heart. Spinoza and those who supported Descartes' philosophy clung to their earlier views of the heart, although they were purely theoretical and lacked scientific proof. They, therefore, failed Descartes' first commandment – that one could only accept that which was obviously certain.

This caused Stensen to appreciate that parts of Descartes' thought was founded upon untenable assumptions and speculation, but still his philosophy regarding methodological doubt and the break from all the usual judgements, exerted a great influence upon him. Many years later, Stensen was asked by Leibnitz if he had found the truths of the Catholic Church in the marrow of bones. Leibnitz had read several of Stensen's scientific works and clearly could not understand why he had converted to the Catholic faith. In a letter to Leibnitz dated 1677, Stensen answers the question. At the same time he explains why his studies of the heart and the construction of muscles made him sceptical of Descartes' philosophy and in the end, resulted in his becoming a Catholic.

> One afternoon, a little later, I drew a comparison between the structure of the heart and that of muscles. I held Descartes' system to be infallible and so took the foot of a rabbit that I had dissected previously, and the first of its muscles I examined revealed to me, from the first incision, the muscle's structure in a way that no-one had previously described. This observation caused the entire Descartes system to disintegrate. The following two truths of far-reaching importance which God revealed to me without any great input on my part produced the following reflections:

1. If these people, whom nearly all who are educated idolize, have held to be incontrovertibly evident, what I, in the course of one hour, can present to a 10 year old boy in such a way that it in an instant – without a word – causes the most ingenious systems of these great intellects, to collapse – what confidence can I have in the other sophistries, that they are so possessed of? When, in this way, they can make such a mistake in relation to material things, that are accessible with the senses, what certainty do I have that they do not also fail when they speak of God and the soul?

2. When God revealed to me the errors of these great minds at a time when I had begun to have the greatest respect for them, one cannot only ascribe this coincidence to God, but must also recognise his goodness. I did not abandon the entire system, because there are still a number of things in it that are true. But gradually I felt liberated from the exaggerated respect I had for these thinkers and I began, to an ever increasing extent, to perceive the frailty of the human intellect. When I was involved in discussions about religion, I eventually summarised my deliberations in the following sentence: either each religion good, or only the Catholic.[(E 143)]

After his death in 1662, Descartes' *De homine* was published. In this work, Descartes describes how the pineal body[11] is the connecting link between the soul and the body. Few scientists of the time doubted this. The news, however, got Stensen to set about dissecting the brains of both humans and animals in order to test the hypothesis put forward by the philosopher. He compared his anatomical findings from the dissections with Descartes' drawings and explanation of the pineal body, but found no agreement between them.

Stensen, with time, became extremely careful about saying anything definitive on matters he had only read

[11] The pineal body lies in the middle of the brain and is about 10cms long and 5cms wide. It looks like a pine cone. In the medical literature it is known as the *epiphysis cerebri* or *corpus pineale*. Its function in humans has not been fully explained.

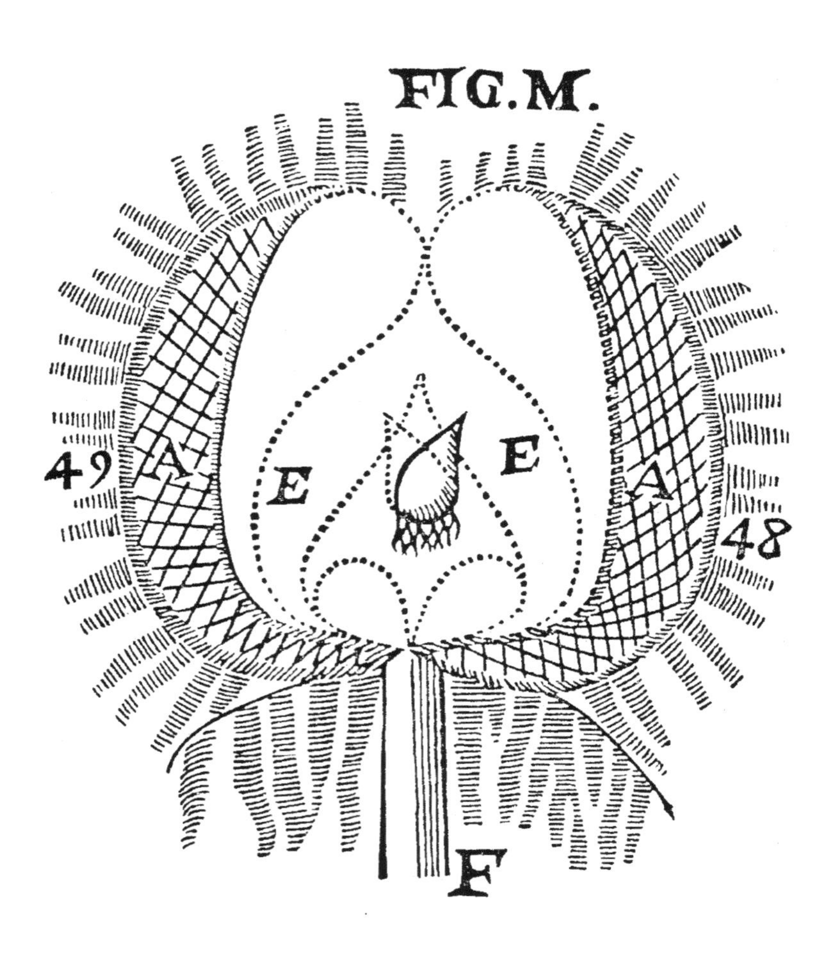

Descartes' illustration of the pineal body (E) in his book *On mankind*, published in 1662, which shows how the movement of the pineal body creates contact between the soul and the body. Stensen showed with his dissections that the pineal body in its natural state cannot move and dismissed Descartes' view as pure.

about and had not himself investigated. A good example is his lecture on the brain where he, who had dissected many brains, openly admitted to his audience that he was not at all certain about how the brain functioned. On this occasion he distances himself publicly, and in all seriousness, from those of Descartes' hypotheses which were not in accordance with the anatomy, and warns against setting up systems which the findings of dissections are expected to adjust to.

Stensen's scientific method

In the lecture introducing his anatomical exercises in Copenhagen in 1673, Stensen says:

> It is not the task of our senses to judge reality such as it actually exists, but they should give reason a basis for judgement. We must not abide by the testimony of our senses but use reason to arrive at a higher understanding.

For Stensen the genuine seeker after truth must acknowledge that, at the outset, he knows nothing for certain. In fact the greater the humility and the fewer prejudices one had, the more knowledge would one acquire in the search for truth. Stensen followed this principle to the letter in his own scientific works. They are all but free of references to other literature, including what he himself had published. The reader was presented only with Stensen's observations and the conclusions he had drawn from them.

In the introduction to *De Solido*, Stensen writes:

> If people travel in unknown territory and struggle forward along rough paths towards a town that lies on a hill top, it can happen that, at the outset, they believe they are quite close. Nevertheless the many bends in the road will delay them and make them cross, indeed, perhaps cause them to abandon hope. They see only the nearest peaks, but in reality the extensive uplands, deep valleys and flat plains are often greater

> than they imagine. The same happens also to the one who wants, through investigations, to attain a true understanding of things. For immediately some of the unknown truth is revealed to them, they believe that they will at once grasp the whole truth.

Put another way: Stensen believes that uplands – or truths – exist that we have no possibility of reaching with our senses, but which, all the same, truly exist.

He draws a clear distinction between that which we can accept as certain and incontrovertible and that which we can only have a presumption of. The conclusions he draws are always provisional and can be changed if new information emerges. He often complains in his letters at having too little time or too little material at his disposal to undertake more observations that could underpin his theories. Characteristically for Stensen, he is never satisfied with examining an organ just from one species, but must compare his observations with comparable organs both from animals and humans. Many of his most important discoveries are the result of comparative work.

Stensen is 'modern' in his demand that an experiment must be able to be repeated with the same result in order to acknowledge its truth. Stensen himself was painstaking, often repeating his dissections in the presence of others in order to show the findings he had made.

In his treatise on the dissection of a shark's head he compares the tongue-like stones with a modern shark's teeth, and to explain how they had been transformed, he makes, as his starting point, six assumptions – conjecturæ – and adopts a presentation that has much in common with that used for mathematical proofs. In his treatise on muscle construction, Stensen shows, with the aid of geometrical figures, that a muscle does not increase in volume when it contracts. The medical doctor Troels Kardel (1994a) has pointed out that this is the first example we know of the use of mathematics in biology.

During his student days in Amsterdam, Stensen's teachers asked him to write a short essay on warm springs, which he should also defend. Such exercises were usual in the presentation and defence of scientific work. In the essay Stensen's argument shows clear signs of being influenced by the scholastic method, commonly used at the time. The method is based on a logical argumentation for and against a particular case, but it has the weakness that it can never give a definitive answer if the empirical starting point is wrong.

Several years later, when Stensen describes phenomena which, in the event, provided the foundation of three new sciences – paleontology, geology and crystallography – he abandoned the scholastic method he had learned in his student days. He is forced to think anew and must develop a general theory of scientific knowledge. Stensen's formulation is based on the work of several of antiquity's philosophers. In the introduction to *De Solido* he gives a description of his approach to scientific knowledge:

> What I have said about matter can be utilised whether one takes it to consist of atoms – or of small parts, which can be changed in countless ways. It applies too if one assumes that the matter is made up of the four elements or of chemical elements that can be determined as accurately as the chemists decide. What I have said about movement applies to each moving force whether it has a physical form or is a mental construct, whether it is ordinary matter or the individual soul or the soul of the world or God's direct involvement.

What is decisive for Stensen is that not all knowledge is empirical, but it is thought that shall be guided by empiricism. In other words not all theoretical understanding needs to be uncertain. From his geological investigations, Stensen discovered that changes in solid matter often left traces and by analysing these the course of the change could be reconstructed. This relationship is called the overlay principle.

The overlay principle

Stensen demonstrated that the earth's strata he studied in Tuscany were created through several changes in solid matter. By interpreting the changes in the strata he was able to distinguish between the older and younger formations in the earth's crust. In this way it was possible for him to form a picture of how the landscape of Tuscany had changed over time. In *De Solido*, Stensen writes:

> Tuscany's landscape is a good example of how the present condition of something can reveal its earlier state, because the unevenness of the terrain provides clear evidence of the changes that have occurred. I will examine these in reverse order in that I go back from the last change to the first.

By interpreting the last change first, it is possible to conceive of how a solid body must have looked before the change occurred. By analysing the different traces in a solid body in reverse order, one is able to describe the changes that have occurred and in this way reconstruct even complex changes and causal relationships. The knowledge we acquire will be for a certain point in time, as it is only the changes that occurred then that can be ascertained. We can, therefore, say nothing certain about periods when no change occurred, as, for instance, how long such periods lasted. In fluids and gasses where molecules are in constant movement, the changes will leave no permanent trace in the material.

To sum up, Stensen's 'overlay principle ' can be formulated as follows: it is only in solid matter that structures are preserved, so making it possible to perceive the changes that have occurred. Our scientific understanding must, therefore, take as its starting point the study of nature's solid matter. According to Stensen, changes in solid objects reveal themselves in such a way that they can be understood immediately by all without any special prior knowledge. If, for example, we see a line drawn on a piece of paper, it is obvious that the paper must have existed before the line. The 'overlay principle ' is based on three axioms : (1) the chronological order criterion (2) the recognition criterion and (3) the preservation criterion.

1. *The Chronological order criterion* can be illustrated with the following quotation from *De Solido:* 'If a solid body is enclosed on all sides by another solid body, it will be the body that first sets, that molds the other through the contact between them to its surface.' When we find a fossilized mussel shell enclosed in slate, it is immediately obvious that the mussel shell must have existed before the slate was formed.
2. With the aid of *analogous conclusions* we can perceive how complicated phenomena have come into existence. Most of us have seen how a snowdrift is formed as the result of the interaction between the impact of the wind on the snow flakes and the unevenness of the ground. If, on a clear day, we see a snow drift, we can permit ourselves to believe that previously snow has fallen and the wind has blown on this spot. In order to come to this conclusion, it is necessary to know about what forces have operated on each of the snow flakes which together make up the snowdrift.
3. *The preservation criterion* is described as follows in *De Solido*: 'If a solid body is just like another solid body – not only as regards its external appearance, but also in the arrangement of its individual parts and in the fine structure of its particles – it will also be like the other body as regards the way it came into existence.'

Two bodies can be like each other in their external appearance, but not in their particles as, for example, an apple and a piece of marble shaped like an apple. They have then also been formed in two quite different ways. Metaphorically they resemble each other but are discordant, because the way they have been formed is different. Stensen was the first to understand the difference between homology and allegory in nature and could draw a distinction between accidental similarities and those that were the result of the fact that they had come into existence in the same way. Two marigolds or two crows are homologous within a certain permissible level of tolerance. The passion flower's likeness to Christ's crown of thorns or the nails on the Cross is a result of coincidence.

Stensen believed, therefore, that if it is possible to separate a phenomenon from its surroundings, then it will also be possible, with certainty to elucidate a complex course of causal relationships. This indicates that Stensen presupposed that there exists a necessary relationship between cause and effect. Our knowledge will be restricted to the changes that have left traces in the solid matter, and this will be conclusive knowledge, which makes it possible to understand the course of previous events. This principle is a challenge to the present day scientific theory of knowledge which presumes that we cannot know anything with absolute certainty, only with a greater or lesser degree of probability.

The unity in the life of Niels Stensen

One can divide Niels Stensen's life into three phases: childhood and youth in Copenhagen, a phase as a scientist of genius and one as a priest and ascetic. Many have deplored the fact that Stensen ceased to be a scientist in order to become a priest and others that he pushed his ascetic life-style so far that it shortened his life.

If, however, we look at the first of his writings of which we can be sure – the 'Chaos' manuscript – we find many features that indicate to us that here we are dealing with a man of faith, firmly rooted in Protestant Christianity. His father came from a family of clergy and the two closest friends of his youth, Jakob Henrik Paulli and Ole Borch, were both men with a deeply held faith. Stensen's belief in a personal God was challenged on several occasions – in his meeting, for example, with Spinoza and Cartesianism. (This subject has been covered in depth by the Stensen scholar Sebastian Olden-Jørgensen (2001).)

The driving force behind Stensen as a scientist was a search for the truth about nature, about the relationship between things and about their origins. He sought with humility – not to exploit the results for his own personal fame , but with the intention of attaining a greater insight into the created and through it the Creator. For Stensen everything hung together and the more one understood the clearer would one understand this connection. There was no contradiction between science and faith in his world view and no clear distinction between the different scientific disciplines. He took it to be just as important to occupy oneself with the study of muscles as with the anatomy of the shark or how the earth's strata were formed. All knowledge was a source of greater understanding of the totality and the beauty of creation. Stensen was convinced that everything he understood through his learning was in accord with his Christian belief. As a researcher he was not afraid to produce discoveries that were sharply at variance with contemporary opinion. He saw clearly the limits of human understanding, both as a natural scientist confronted with the visible world and as a believer confronted with God's plan for creation. He saw God's divine providence in all the vicissitudes be experienced in his own life.

Niels Stensen is spoken of by some people as a personality who threw himself with a restless energy into one research project after another. There is something in this, for his research field was very broad. Nevertheless Niels Stensen completed most of the things he worked upon. He himself gave to his most epoch-making work on geology, the sub-title *provisional report* – all the same he managed to write down his most important discoveries and conclusions.

It is true that there are many examples in Stensen's life of his being forced to give up one task in order to take on others, and, it goes without saying, that this gives the impression of an element of unsteadiness in his character. There is, however, no doubt that Niels Stensen increasingly saw his own situation as a long pilgrimage. The old adage that 'the path comes into being only when one walks along it' could have been seen as the common denominator of his life. It was life here and now that was important for him. He shared his thoughts and his material goods with the people he met on his way, without thinking especially about what tomorrow would bring. Consequentially, Stensen's determination to live according to what he perceived as being true, runs like a red thread through the whole of his life – both as a natural scientist and a Christian. Ibsen's words about 'being complete and whole, not piecemeal and divided' could also have been Stensen's motto.

During the last years of his life in Schwerin, Stensen managed to write down a number of prayers that were used for domestic worship. The book, the so-called Schwerin Prayer Book still exists and the following prayer which bears the name *Niels Stensen's Prayer*, illustrates how he construed his life.

> Without a sign from You not a hair falls from the head, not a leaf from the tree, not a bird to the ground, no thought escapes from the mind, no word from the tongue, and no movement is made by the hand.
>
> You have hitherto led me along roads I knew not. Lead me now on the path of grace, seeing or blind. It is easier for You to guide me there, where You will, than for me to withdraw from that my yearnings draw me towards.

Chronology

1st January 1638	Born in Copenhagen
1647–56	Pupil at The School of Our Lady
1655–59	Medical student at Copenhagen University
1658–60	Further studies at Rostock and Amsterdam
7th April 1660	Discovers the parotid duct
1659–63	Studies at the University of Leiden
1663–66	Studies in France
1665	Delivers lecture on the brain in Paris
1665–66	Visits Montpellier
1666–68	First visit to Italy. Undertakes research in anatomy, paleontology, mineralogy and geology
2nd November 1667	Converts to the Catholic faith
1667–70	Studies mining in south-east Europe, visits Amsterdam
1670–72	Second visit to Italy. First publications in theology. Continues geological research

1672–74	Royal anatomist in Copenhagen
1675–77	Third visit to Italy. Priest in Florence, tutor to the son of the Grand Duke of Tuscany
1675	Ordained priest on Easter Eve
19th September 1677	Consecrated bishop in Rome
1677–80	Vicar Apostolic in Hanover
1680–83	Auxiliary bishop in Münster and Paderborn
1683–85	Vicar Apostolic in Hamburg
1685	Last visit to Copenhagen
1685–86	Missionary in Schwerin
5th December 1686	Dies in Schwerin
1687	Buried in the Church of San Lorenzo, Florence
23rd October 1953	Placed in sarcophagus in the Capella Stenonia, Church of San Lorenzo
23rd October 1988	Beatified in St Peters, Rome

Bibliography

Aggebo, Anker: *Danmarks store søn Niels Stensen 1638–1938 : Et mindeskrift*, Universitetsforlaget, Århus, 1937.

Bendix-Almgren, Svend Erik: 'Stor, Større – Carcharodon megalodon : En ganske særlig hajtand fra Gram-leret', *Sønderjydske museer* 9 (1982): 15–37.

Bierbaum, Max, Faller, Adolf og Traeger, Josef: *Niels Stensen – Anatom, Geologe und Bischof 1638–1686*, 3 ed. Aschendorff, Münster, 1989.

Bjarnhof, Karl: *Støv skal du blive : På spor av Niels Steensen*, Gyldendal, Copenhagen, 1972.

Christensen, R. E., Hansen, Axel og Larsen, Knud: *Niels Steensens (Stenonis) Værker i Oversættelse*, vol. I, Copenhagen, 1939.

Cioni, Rafaello: *Niels Stensen Scientist – Bishop*, P. J. Kenedy & Sons, New York, 1962.

Cohen, C: 'Un manuscript inédit de Leibniz sur la nature des objèts fossiles', *Bull. Soc. Géol. Fr*, 1 (1998) 137–142.

Faller, Adolf: 'Niels Stensen und der Cartesianismus', in *Nicolaus Steno and his Indice*, Acta Historica Scientarium Naturalium et medicinalium, ed. G. Scherz, 15 (Copenhagen: Munksgaard, 1958), pp. 140–166.

Garboe, Axel: 'Niels Stensen (Nicolaus Steno)', in *Geologiens historie i Danmark I : Fra myte til videnskab*, ed. A. Garboe, C. A. Reitzels Forlag, Copenhagen, 1959, pp. 50–75.

Garboe, Axel: 'Niels Stensens (Stenos) geologiske Arbejders Skæbne : Et fragment af Dansk Geologis Historie', *Danmarks Geologiske Undersøgelser*, series IV, vol. 3 (1948), 1–34.

Gorschenek, Margareta: *Niels Stensen Glauben & Wissen : Einheit oder Widerspruch ?* Katholishe Akademie Hamburg, Hamburg, 1986.

Hansen, Harriet Merete: *Niels Stensen's korrespondance i dansk oversættelse*, C. A. Reitzels Forlag, Copenhagen, 1987.
Hansen, Jens Morten: *Stregen i sandet, bølgen på vandet – Stenos teori om naturens sprog og erkendelsens grænser*, Fremad, Copenhagen, 2000. ISBN: 97–557–2299–7.
Jensen, Michael: *Bibliographia Nicolai Stensonis*, Impetus, Mørke 1986. A bibliography that aims to cover the literature by and about Stensen from his own time to 1986. The literature is arranged chronologically and comprises over 6,000 items.
Jørgensen, A. D.: *Nils Stensen : et mindeskrift*, Samfundet til den danske litteraturs fremme., Copenhagen, 1884.
Kallan, Kaspar: 'Wie Heisst Niels Steensen eigentlich? : Dänische Namessitten in 17. Jahrhundert', *Stenoniana Nova Series* 1 (1991), 152–156.
Kardel, Troels: 'Niels Stensens hjerneforskning', *Videnskabsforskning* 17 (1997), 9–13.
Kardel, Troels: *Steno : Life – Science – Philosophy*, Acta Historica Scientarium Naturalium et Medicinalium., vol. 42, Munksgaard, Copenhagen, 1994.
Kardel, Troels: *Steno on Muscles*, Transactions of the American Philosophical Society ed. vol. 84 part 1, The American Philosophical Society, Philadelphia, 1994.
Kardel, Troels: 'Niels Stensen's muskelteori genopdaget. Et videnskabeligt gennembrud med forsinkelser', *Naturens verden* 1991 (1991), 453–461.
Kardel, Troels: 'Niels Stensen's Geometrical Theory of Muscle Contraction (1667): A Reappraisal', *Journal of Biomechanics* 23 (1990), 953–965.
Kermit, Hans: 'Niels Steensen og Norge', *St Olav* 108 (1996), 17–19.
Kermit, Hans: 'The Oneness in Niels Stensen's Life', *Analecta Romana Instituti Danici Supplementum* XXXI (2002), 23–26.
Kognsted, Ole, Rasmussen, Jørgen Nybo og Ziggelaar, August: *Niels Stensen og Danmark – Kirkens fattige tjener*, Katolsk Forlag, Copenhagen, 1981.
Kranz, Gisbert: 'Niels Steensen 1638–1686 videnskab og tro', in *7 kristne der skabte fornyelse i verden*, ed. G. Kranz, Verlag Pustet, Regensburg, 1977, pp. 159–184.
Kuhne, Alexander: *Niels Stensen – Anatom Geologe Bischof – Ein Seliger des Erzbistums Paderborn*, Bonifatius Druck Buch Verlag, Paderborn, 1989.

Meisen, V.: 'Michael Servetus', in *Medicinsk historiske afhandlinger og portrætter*, ed. V. Meisen, Levin & Munksgaards Forlag, Copenhagen, 1933, pp. 119–146.

Moe, Harald: *Nicolaus Steno – An Illustrated Biography – His Tireless Pursuit of Knowledge – His Genius – His Quest for the Absolute*, Rhodos, Copenhagen, 1994. ISBN: 87–7245–582–9.

Mortensen, Miriam: *Skønnest af alt : En biografi om Niels Steensen*, Katolsk Forlag, Copenhagen, 1993. ISBN: 87–85213–50-0.

Olden-Jørgensen, Sebastian: 'Videnskabelig erfaring og religiøs erkendelse hos Niels Steensen', *AC revue* 7 (1998), 24–27.

Olden-Jørgensen, Sebastian: *Niels Steensens sentenser og spiritualitet*, Ælnoth's writings, no. 2, Ælnoth, Grenå, 1992.

Olden-Jørgensen, Sebastian: 'Die Konversjon Niels Steensens (1667) under der Frühneuzeitliche Deismus', *Historiches Jahrbuch*, Freiburg and Munich 121 (2001): 97–114.

Pålsson, Erik Kennet: *Niels Stensen – Scientist and Saint*, Oscott Series 2, Veritas, Dublin, 1988.

Plenkers, Willhelm: *Der Däne Niels Stensen : Ein Lebensbild*, Herder, Freiburg, 1884.

Plovgaard, Karen: *Niels Stensen, anatom, geolog og biskop*, Pauluskredsen, Copenhagen, 1953.

Pontificia Academia Scientiarum: *Blessed Niels Stensen and His Memorial Plaque in the Pontifical Academy of Sciences*, Ex Aedibvs Academicis in Civitate Vaticana, Citta del Vaticano, MCMLXXXIX. ISBN: 88–7761-035–2.

Poulsen, Jacob E. og Snorrason, Egill: *Nicolaus Steno 1638 – 1686: A re-consideration by Danish Scientists*, Nordisk Insulinlaboratorium, Copenhagen, 1989.

Røger, Magnus: 'Niels Stensen – vår nye nordiske helgen', *St Olav* 96 (1988) 3–8.

Rørdam, Holger: *De danske og norske Studenters Deltagelse i Kjøbenhavns Forsvar mod Karl Gustav*, Copenhagen, 1855.

Rose, Johannes: *Nicolaus Stenos liv og død*, Vilhelm Trydes Forlag, Copenhagen, 1906.

Rosenkilde, Volmer: 'Niels Steensen', in *Gamle danske bøger af international berømmelse*, ed. V. Rosenkilde, Levin & Munksgaard, Copenhagen, 1933, pp. 31–42.

Schepelern, H. D.: *Niels Stensen. En dansk student i 1659 og noterne i hans Chaos-manuskript*, Katolsk Forlag, Copenhagen, 1986.

Scherz, Gustav: *Niels Stensen : Eine Biographie Band I-II*, St Benno-Verlag GmbH, Leipzig, 1988.

Scherz, Gustav: *Steno*, G.E.C. Gads Forlag, Copenhagen, 1963a.

Scherz, Gustav: 'Niels Stensens Copenhagen', *Geologisk information* 37 (1963b), 1–40.

Scherz, Gustav: *Nicolaus Steno and his Indice*, Acta Historica Scientarium Naturalium et Medicinalium, vol. 15, Munksgaard, Copenhagen, 1958.

Scherz, Gustav (ed.): *Steno Geological Papers*, Acta Historica Scientarium Naturalium et Medicinalium, vol. 20, Odense University Press, 1969.

Scherz, Gustav and Beck, Peter: *Niels Steensen (Nicolaus Steno) 1638–1686*, Royal Danish Ministry of Foreign Affairs, Copenhagen, 1988. ISBN: 87–87646–36–6.

Schjelderup, H. K. and Winsnes, A. H.: *Den eropeiske filosofi : Fra middelalderen til vår tid*, 3 ed. Gyldendal, Oslo, 1966.

Steno, Nicolaus: *Nicolaus Steno's Lecture on the Anatomy of the Brain*, Nyt Nordisk Forlag Arnold Busck, Copenhagen, 1965.

Steno, Nicolaus: 'Dissektion af et hajhoved ved V. Meisen', *Stenoniana* 1 (1933a) 50–98.

Steno, Nicolaus: 'Indledningsforelæsning til demonstationerne i Copenhagens Anatomiske Teater 1673', *Stenoniana* 1 (1933) 100–111.

Steno, Nicolaus: *Foredrag om Hjærnens anatomi*, tr. Vilhelm Maar, Copenhagen, 1903.

Steno, Nicolaus: *Foreløpig meddelelse til en afhandling om faste legemer, der findes naturlig indlejrede i andre faste legemer*, Gyldendalske Boghandels Forlag, Copenhagen, 1902.

Stenonis, Nicolai: *Epistolae I–II*, ed. G. Scherz adjuvante J. Ræder, Hafniae et Friburgi, 1952.

Stenonis, Nicolai: *Opera Theologica I–II :* ed. Knud Larsen et Gustav Scherz, Hafniae et Friburgi, 1941.

Stenonis, Nicolai: *Opera Philosophica I–II*, ed. Vilhelm Maar, Copenhagen, 1910.

Stensen, Niels: *Foredrag om Hjernens Anatomi : held in Paris 1665 and printed in the same place in 1669*, Troels Kardel, Nyt Nordisk Forlag Arnold Busck, Copenhagen, 1997. ISBN: 87–17–06706–5.

Stensen, Niels: *Steno in Six Languages*, Rhodos, Copenhagen, 1986. ISBN: 87–7245–160–2.

Stensen, Niels: *Steno Geological Papers*, Acta Historica Scientarium Natuaralium et Medicinalium, vol. 20, Odense University Press, Odense, 1969.

Stensen, Niels: *Niels Stensen in seinen Schriften (Pioner der Wissenschaft), Auswahl und Übersetzung von G. Scherz*, Copenhagen, 1963.

Totaro, Pina: 'Ho certi amici in Ollandia?' – Stensen and Spinoza – science verso faith, *Analecta Romana Instituti Danici*, Supplementum XXXI (2002), 27–38.

Wagner, Peter Henrik: 'Steno and Ray: Two Geologists and Men of Faith', in *Nicolaus Steno 1638–1686 : A Re-consideration by Danish Scientists*, ed. J. E. Poulsen and E. Snorrason, Nordisk Insulinlaboratorium, Copenhagen, 1986, pp. 153–166.

Wieh, Hermann: *Niels Stensen : Sein Leben in Dokumenten und Bildern*, Echter Verlag, Würzburg, 1988.

Zanna, Lorenzo, Grégoire, Pierre, Kallan, Kaspar, Olden-Jørgensen, Sebastian and Snorrasson, Egill: *Stenoniana Nova Series*, Lægeforeningens Forlag, Copenhagen, 1991.

Ziggelaar, August: *Chaos : Niels Stensen's Chaos-manuskript Copenhagen, 1659 complete edition with Introduction, Notes and Commentary*, Acta Historica Scientiarium Naturalium et Medicinalium ed., vol. 44, Munksgaard, Copenhagen, 1997.

Index of Names

Index of Places